CLASS

FRANK BRENNAN

HEINEMANN
SPOTLIGHTS

Heinemann Educational

Heinemann Educational Publishers
Halley Court, Jordan Hill, Oxford OX2 8EJ
a division of Reed Educational & Professional Publishing Ltd

MELBOURNE   AUCKLAND
FLORENCE   PRAGUE   MADRID   ATHENS
SINGAPORE   TOKYO   SAO PAULO
CHICAGO   PORTSMOUTH (NH)   MEXICO
IBADAN   GABORONE   JOHANNESBURG
KAMPALA   NAIROBI

ISBN 0 435 23904 X

97 98 99 10 9 8 7 6 5

Dedication
For Pamela

Printed in England by Clays Ltd, St Ives plc

CONTENTS

Introduction   3
The Bikers' Ballad   5
The Lucky Lion   20
Wishful Thinking   37
How to Steal a Troll's Trombone   51
Benny and the Woodwose   55
Playing for Time   82

INTRODUCTION

It is not always easy to find a play of the right length for use in class or on the stage. I decided to tackle this problem by writing six comedies which vary in length and in the size of their casts.

The plays were written to be flexible, so if you need to make changes to fit the requirements of your particular class, please do so. Most of all, have fun.

Frank Brennan
June 1991

The Bikers' Ballad

CHARACTERS

OLD MAN/OLD WOMAN *who is the narrator*
CAFE OWNER/DEVIL
BIKER ONE ⎫
BIKER TWO ⎭ *Brothers*
BIKER THREE, *girlfriend of Biker One*

SCENE 1: A seaside cafe
SCENE 2: A hill in the nearby countryside

Properties
Several beer cans
One brandy bottle
One flick knife
Cartons, plates etc. for curry
One rock
One dead tree
Two large boxes, one filled with money
One portable cassette player
Three pairs of devils' horns
One pitchfork
Tables, chairs etc. for cafe
Leather gear for bikers and cafe owner

The Bikers' Ballad

Prologue

Stage is in darkness except for spotlight to one side. Enter OLD MAN, *carrying a book with 'Cautionary Tales' written in large letters on the cover. He addresses the audience.*

OLD MAN: There's a story I know, written long long
　　　　　ago,
　　　　And it's often enacted today –
　　　　About greed, which can crumble both high
　　　　　folks and humble,
　　　　In an 'orrible, 'orrible way.
　　　　And to prove it applies and I'm not telling lies
　　　　(For you know that it's lies that I hate)
　　　　Let's all take a look at the tale in this book
　　　　Of three villains, their greed . . . and their
　　　　　fate.

　　Spotlight goes out. Exit OLD MAN *carrying the open
book.*

Scene 1

A seaside cafe. Lights come up to reveal the cafe, where BIKER 1 *and* BIKER 3 *are seated, drinking beer from cans or bottles. The cafe owner is washing glasses in the background – he or she has two black eyes. The rest of the cafe is empty. Heavy-metal music is being played on a cassette-player.*

BIKER 3 (*in a whining voice, as she switches off the cassette player*):

> Aw, come on darlin', this is borin'.
> I'd rather hear me granny snorin'.
> Let's take our bikes and find some action!

BIKER 1:   Look, girl, I'll put your mouth in traction!
> It's one moan followed by another –

BIKER 3:   And then there's your great stupid brother
> Hangin' round like an albatross –

BIKER 1:   Now get this straight, doll, I'm the boss –

BIKER 3:   Oh yeah?

BIKER 1:   – and I don't give a toss
> What you think! Let me tell you,
> Stop your whinging or we're through!
> He's bought the drinks, so try saying thanks.

BIKER 3:   But he's as thick as two short planks!
> Why not take him for a ride?

BIKER 1:   'Cos he's all I got since me old Mum died,
> And I promised then outside the church
> I'd never leave him in the lurch.
> Now don't be rotten, leave him be –

BIKER 3:   You *could* leave him and go with *me* . . .
> Your biker's moll, your faithful steady!
> (*voice now raucous*) Let's leave the creep – he's
> drunk already!

BIKER 1 (*to himself and the audience*):

> She's right, I'm not my brother's keeper,
> I'd just as soon have her – she's cheaper!
> And as for promises, once they're spoken,
> All they're fit for's to be broken.

The sound of a motorbike off-stage, followed by loud sounds of clattering dustbins and whooping cries. Enter BIKER 2 *with beer cans in one hand and a bottle of spirits in the other – he holds them up triumphantly.*

BIKER 2:   Ta da!

BIKER 1 (*to audience*):

                    Oh no! 'E's off again,
                    One big stomach and half a brain!

BIKER 2:   Export lager and Japanese brandy –
                    And I didn't have to pay!

BIKER 1:   That's handy.
                    Why?

BIKER 2:   'Cos that's what the little man said,
                    Straight after I bashed 'im on the 'ead!

BIKER 1:   And your bike? Where did you park it?

BIKER 2:   It got crunched outside the supermarket.
                    (*Laughs loudly*) Good job I found another
                       outside the shop
                    Donated by a traffic cop.

BIKER 1:   A traffic cop! You've bashed the Bill?

BIKER 2:   I didn't know 'is name – but still,
                    'E won't mind now, 'e's fast asleep –
                    And what I find is mine to keep!

    BIKER 2 *sits noisily, begins to open the beer. The* CAFE OWNER *steps forward as the bikers laugh among themselves.*

OWNER (*to audience*):

                    These thugs, they think they own the place
                    Once the pub's shut, it's a disgrace
                    The way they shout and drink their beer –
                    They scare my customers out of here!
                    They rob my takings, eat my food –

BIKER 3 (*to cafe owner*):

                    Hey mush! Don't gawp – it's rude!
                    Now close the door or I'll catch me death.

    CAFE OWNER *closes the door.*

OWNER (*to audience*):

> I daren't complain – it's a waste of breath.
> The last time I tried to with these guys
> They laughed and gave me two black eyes!

He points to his eyes and then goes back to his counter.

BIKER 1:　　Listen! Now Einstein 'ere has robbed a copper
　　　　　　We'll 'ave to split or come a cropper.

BIKER 2:　　Who's Einstein?

BIKER 1 (*impatiently*):

> 'E's a relative, see –

BIKER 2 (*angry and confused*):

> What's 'e got to do with me?

BIKER 3:　　Calm down, love, your brother's right!
　　　　　　We'll have to scarper soon – tonight!

BIKER 2 (*to audience*):

> She called me 'love'! Has she heard
> I've always fancied me brother's bird?
> I'll 'ave a beer to celebrate! (*picks up can*)

BIKER 1 (*to* BIKER 2):

> Put it down! Can't you wait?
> Now listen, we need lots of cash –

BIKER 2 (*angrily*):

> No, *you* listen! I'm gonna bash –

BIKER 3 (*trying to calm him down*):

> Now hold it, big boy, just sit down.
> We need some cash to get out of town.

BIKER 2 (*to audience*):

> She called me 'big boy'! I'm so proud!
> But with 'im around (*indicates his brother*)
> 　　three's a crowd.
> (*to* BIKER 1) All right, then, brother, what's
> 　　your plan?

BIKER 1 *opens his mouth to speak but before he can say a word the* OLD MAN *staggers in, panting, exhausted and dishevelled.*

OLD MAN: Help!

BIKER 2: Who's that?

BIKER 1: We're not acquainted.

OLD MAN: Help!

BIKER 3: Look out!

OWNER: He's gone and fainted!
Help me put him on a chair!

BIKER 2: I wouldn't take him anywhere!
What a scruff! Phew, what a pong!

BIKER 1: Come on! you two. It won't take long.

They help the OLD MAN *to a chair.*

OLD MAN (*gasping*):
Water! Water!

BIKER 2: Where?

BIKER 1: You twerp!
'E wants a drink – (to CAFE OWNER) give
'im a slurp.

CAFE OWNER *gives him some water.*

OWNER (*to* OLD MAN):
You look half-starved! I'll fix you a curry.

CAFE OWNER *goes off to get it.*

BIKER 3: Yeah, that'll finish him off in a hurry!

BIKER 1: Grandad, you're white as a lump of suet.

BIKER 3: Yeah, who scared you?

BIKER 2: And how did he do it?

OLD MAN: Just let me catch another breath.
Alas, I've just escaped from Death!

BIKER 3: Blimey – 'e don't 'alf talk funny!

OLD MAN: He tempted me with all that money.

ALL THE BIKERS:
Money??

BIKER 1:   Tell us more, old friend.
(*to the other* BIKERS) Some cash would be a
    real godsend!

OLD MAN: Money tempts us, brings disasters!
    Our souls were meant for heavenly pastures.
    And besides, it's worthless trash –
    So I left the Devil and all his cash!

BIKER 2: You left some cash . . .!

BIKER 1:   Now just calm
    down.
(*to* OLD MAN) Er – is this money still in
    town?
(*piously*) We can see the harm it must be doin'.
    We'd like to save more souls from ruin.

OLD MAN: My children, think of *your* souls first –
    Don't let the Devil do his worst!

BIKER 2 (*to* BIKER 1):
    'Ere, this geezer's Brahms and Liszt!

BIKER 3: Or some born-again fundamentalist!

BIKER 1 (*to other* BIKERS):
    Let's humour him – he might be mad,
    But *any* chance of cash ain't bad.
(*to* OLD MAN) To get back to our
    conversation –

OLD MAN: Oh, turn away from this temptation!
    Think of your souls – you're still young yet.
    If you look for gold it's Death you'll get!

BIKER 3: Hey, Grandad, you're a laugh a minute.

BIKER 2: Gold . . .

BIKER 1:   There may be something in it.

BIKER 2 (*to* OLD MAN):
    Bashing you would be a pleasure –

BIKER 3: Tell us where to find the treasure!

BIKER 2: – tell us now or you're dead meat!

BIKER 1 (*to other* BIKERS):
    Dead subtle! That'll work a treat!

OLD MAN: If you insist –

BIKER 2: ⎫
BIKER 3: ⎭   We do! We do!

BIKER 1:   Well I never! Count me in too! (*He laughs.*)

OLD MAN: Outside, upon that hill you'll see
           A rock beside an old dead tree.
           Behind that rock, if you've the nerve,
           You're sure to find what you deserve.

BIKER 2:   Now you're talking!

BIKER 3:   Right!

BIKER 1:   Let's split!

Exit all three BIKERS *laughing excitedly.*

OLD MAN (*sadly*):
           I wish I'd never mentioned it!

He slumps over the table. Lights down.

Scene 2

The top of the hill. There is a dead tree and a rock. Enter the BIKERS, *out of breath.*

BIKER 1:   This looks like it.

BIKER 3:   At last we're here!

BIKER 2 (*searching his pockets*):
           Stone me – I've just run out of beer . . .

BIKER 3:   I'm knackered! Cor – me feet are steamin'.
           Treasure here? You must be dreamin'!
           This place is rubbish – what a tip!

BIKER 1:   Oh, stop your moaning – button your lip!
           None of us is used to hiking
           But this hill's been too steep for biking.

    BIKER 2 *starts drinking spirits.*

BIKER 3:   Oh no, he's started on the liquor!

BIKER 2 (*to audience*):
           That's better – quickens up the ticker!

                    (*looking longingly at* BIKER 3) That
                        dreamgirl's wasted on that twit.

BIKER 1:   Oi! You two! Move about a bit!
              The money's here, the old bird said.

BIKER 3:   What if he was soft in the 'ead?
              A mental case. (*To* BIKER 2) Ain't that right,
              pet?

BIKER 2 (*to audience*):
              She called me pet! I won't forget!

BIKER 3:   'E was barmy! (*to* BIKER 2) Wasn't 'e, love?

BIKER 2:   She called me love! Oh 'eavens above,
              I'm the man whose love will kill 'er!

BIKER 1 (*to* BIKER 3):
              Don't humour him, the stupid gorilla.
              Let's start looking.

BIKER 3 (*sulkily*):   Oh, all right.
              But I'm not staying here tonight.

They hunt around. BIKER 1 *finds a box behind the rock.*

BIKER 1:   I've found a box! I've found the cash!

BIKER 3:   Well don't just stand there! Give it a bash!

BIKER 1 *strikes the box. It opens. He turns it upside down. It is empty.*

BIKER 3 (*sarcastically*):
              An empty box! On dear oh dear!

BIKER 2 *notices another box behind the tree.*

BIKER 2:   Another box! Look over here!

He brings it out. It is obviously heavy.

BIKER 2:   Gor blimey! This one weighs a ton!

BIKER 1 (*excitedly*):
              Let's open it at once, my son!

BIKER 2 *opens the box. It is filled with money – coins or notes. The bikers are stunned at first, then realise their good fortune.*

BIKER 2:   We're rich!
BIKER 1:   We're wealthy!
BIKER 3:   Is it real?
BIKER 1:   Course it is! 'Ere, 'ave a feel!
            This ain't the work of any forgers,
            Don't you see? Oh, kiss me, gorgeous!

He kisses BIKER 3.

BIKER 2 (*to audience*):
            Just look at that, the slimy toad!
            (*to* BIKER 1) How do we get this on the road?
            I'm hungry and I need a drink,
            And so does she!
BIKER 1:   You're right, let's think.
            I tell you what, if you'll just wait,
            I'll get some beer, we'll celebrate!
            And while I'm at it, I'll get us a curry.
BIKER 3:   Yeah, take your time, you needn't worry –
            The money's safe with us all right!
            Just be back before tonight.
            Well, off you go then! (*She pushes* BIKER 1) –
              Make a start!
BIKER 1:   I'll see you later. 'Bye, sweetheart!

Exit BIKER 1, *followed by nasty looks from* BIKER 2.

BIKER 3 (*to audience*):
            Sweetheart, me? The stupid wally!
            I'd just as soon have all the lolly!
            I've got a plan – I'll start it quick . . .
            (*to* BIKER 2, *in exaggerated tones*) The boring
              wimp! He makes me sick!
BIKER 2:   Boring wimp?
BIKER 3:   Oh yes, it's true!
            Your brother's a drip – I fancy you!
BIKER 2:   You do?
BIKER 3:   Of course! But it's too late –
BIKER 2:   Too late?

BIKER 3:	Too late to take the money And emigrate to somewhere sunny.
BIKER 2:	Why not?
BIKER 3:	Why not? Can't you guess? Your brother's in the way! . . . Unless . . .
BIKER 2:	Unless?
BIKER 3:	Unless you show you're clever, And get him off our backs – *forever!*
BIKER 2:	I'm clever, darlin' – give us a kiss!
BIKER 3:	Later! Later! First take this!

BIKER 3 *hands* BIKER 2 *a knife.*

BIKER 2:	A knife!
BIKER 3:	That's right! You catch on quick!
BIKER 2:	And to think my brother says I'm thick!
BIKER 3:	This 'ere knife is razor-sharp – That twit will soon be playing a harp If you stab 'im till 'e twitches – An operation without stitches! For all I care he can go to hell. You can have his cash . . . and *me* as well!
BIKER 2:	You've always loved me! I just knew it!
BIKER 3:	Now listen to me – here's how we do it.

They sit down by the tree in a conspiratorial manner and 'freeze'. Enter the OLD MAN.

OLD MAN (*to audience*):

While these villains were busily hatching their
  plot
With dastardly, murderous guile,
The third one was thinking of what he had
  got,
And smiling an evil smile.
You see, he'd brought beer to bring them all
  cheer
But the take-away curry was rough –

> For although he'd made sure that *his* portion
>   was clear . . .
> He'd poisoned the rest of the stuff!

Exit OLD MAN. BIKERS 2 *and* 3 *'unfreeze'. Enter*
BIKER 1 *carrying beer and curry.*

BIKER 1 (*to audience*):
> Why waste all that cash on King Kong and
>   that tart?
> I'll poison 'em both and make a fresh start!
>   (*Gives a villainous cackle*)
> (*to the other two*) Come on, my darlings,
>   loverly grub –
> Take-away curry and beer from the pub!

BIKER 3 (*hugging* BIKER 1):
> Ta love – *we'll* like it anyhow . . .
> But *you* won't!

BIKER 2 has crept up menacingly behind BIKER 1.

BIKER 1:   Why not?

BIKER 2 grabs BIKER 1 *round his neck.*

BIKER 2:   Gotcha!

BIKER 3 jumps clear of BIKER 1 *and* BIKER 2 *has drawn
his knife.*

BIKER 3:   Now!

BIKER 2 stabs BIKER 1, *who slumps to the ground.*

BIKER 3:   You deserve a kiss – here, have this smacker!

BIKER 3 kisses BIKER 1, *who groans and dies.*

BIKER 2 (*sounding self-satisfied*):
> His spine snapped like a Christmas cracker!

BIKERS 2 and 3 both laugh.

BIKER 3 (*to audience*):
> Now that this one's croaked his last
> I'll send this moron after him – fast! (*She giggles.*)
> (*to* BIKER 2) You're my hero! You're dead cool!
> You showed that creep you're nobody's fool!
> (*to audience*) Muscles 'ere can shift the treasure,
> Then I can stab him at my leisure!
> (*to* BIKER 2) 'Ave a kiss then, you deserve it!

She kisses BIKER 2.

BIKER 2:
> 'Ere's more delights – now 'elp me serve it.
> 'E won't be needing 'is in a hurry,
> So come on, darlin', eat up your curry!

They laugh, and set to eating the curry.

BIKER 3: Oh good, my favourite – vindaloo!
BIKER 2: I've eaten mine – I'll 'ave 'is too.

They eat all the curry, and BIKER 2 *burps loudly.*

BIKER 2:
> That was good – now give us a kiss,
> Then you can help me spend all this.

They laugh, but suddenly BIKER 2 *clutches his stomach, quickly followed by* BIKER 3.

BIKER 2 (*in a childish voice*):
> My tummy 'urts – oh, 'elp me, Mum!

BIKER 2 *dies.*

BIKER 3: 'E's poisoned us, the dirty scum!

BIKER 3 *dies; enter the* OLD MAN. *Lights dim except for the spotlight on him.*

OLD MAN: And that, my good friends, is how our story ends;

Their souls are condemned to a roastin'.
They might've been sharing and decent and
    caring,
But they weren't, so that's why they're
    toastin'.
If they'd listened to me, their souls would be
    free,
But did they listen? Oh, no!
I was wasting me breath – instead they found
    Death.

Lights gradually come up again.

OLD MAN (*to the bodies*):
        Ah well, I told you so!

OLD MAN *shakes his head and looks pious. The bodies of
the three* BIKERS *rise up. They are ghosts from hell and have
little horns on their heads – easily hidden behind one of the other
props in readiness for this scene.*

BIKER 2:   I stabbed me brother! (*Puts his head in his
            hands*) I am slime!
BIKER 3:   And I was a partner to the crime!
BIKER 1:   I was naughty! I was rude!
            I put rat-poison in their food!
BIKER 2:   If in life we'd not been louts
BIKER 3:   And joined the Girl Guides –
BIKER 2:   – or the Scouts
BIKER 3:   If we'd been honest and discreet,
            And helped old ladies cross the street
BIKER 1:   We'd still be living well-contented –
            But now by devils we're tormented!
BIKER 2:   And of all the torments that we suffer
BIKER 3 (*pointing at the* OLD MAN):
            There's none that's worse that this old duffer
BIKER 1:   Looking at us, here below . . .

BIKER 1; ⎫
BIKER 2: ⎬ And saying that he told us so! Aagh!
BIKER 3: ⎭

Enter a devil, looking like the CAFE OWNER *but wearing a biker's jacket, sunglasses and carrying a pitchfork. The devil pokes at the* BIKERS *with the pitchfork and sends them screaming off the stage. Devil pauses to share a confidential chuckle with the* OLD MAN *and the audience. Exit the devil followed by the* OLD MAN; *lights down.*

[*Curtain*]

The Lucky Lion

A Play for Chinese New Year

CHARACTERS

TONGPO, *a young farmer*
HONG BAU, *Tongpo's brother*
TO MA TO, *the village head*
FAN TONG, *the village cook*
RATTAN, *the village basket-maker*
RUN WAI, *a farmer*
MA CHO, *a farmer*
POH TEE, *the village potter*
MU MU, *the village carpenter*
BEAST
NARRATOR

In the original Chinese legend all these characters were male, but there is no reason why any of them – with the obvious exception of MA CHO – cannot be played by girls. The only necessary alterations to the script (apart from 'he', 'him', 'his', etc.) would be TONGPO's references to HONG BAU as 'Brother'. Use whatever combination of boys and girls suits the class.

Tong Po is the original name used in the source material for the hero of the legend. Hong Bao is Chinese for 'red packet' – a reference to Chinese New Year gifts, usually of money, that are traditionally given in red envelopes. Fan Tong is Chinese for 'big mouth'. Mu Mu is Chinese for 'wood', and Rattan is a kind of cane used for making furniture and baskets.

SCENES 1 & 3: Fields outside the village
SCENE 2: A village

Properties
Mask for Beast
Lion Dance outfit for Tongpo and Hong Bau
   (just a mask will do if need be)
Black cut–out for Beast's 'footprint'
Basket for the trap
Hammer
Various pots, pans, gongs etc
Transistor radio (or box resembling one)

Pronunciation
'Hong Bau' is pronounced 'Hong Bow'.
'Run Wai' is pronounced 'Run Way'.
'Gong Xi Fa Cai' is pronounced 'Gong See Fah Chy' (Chy
   as in 'why').

Scene 1

A field outside the village. All of the cast apart from TONGPO, HONG BAU and NARRATOR can take part in this. Each person stands straight with his hands up in the air. They represent a field full of wheat. There should be at least five or six people representing this 'harvest'. They stand still for about ten seconds before the NARRATOR enters. Enter NARRATOR.

NARRATOR: Many years ago in old China there was a small farming village. The people of the village depended on their crops for their livelihood. They were proud of their tall wheat which would sway in the wind as if impatient to be harvested.

   The 'harvest' sways.

NARRATOR: Then, one moonlit night when all the villagers were asleep . . .

   Short spell of loud snoring from the wings.

NARRATOR: . . . a strange thing happened: a huge animal with a great mane and fierce eyes came to the field of wheat, and danced . . .

   Enter BEAST, dancing either disco-style to a walkman/ portable radio-cassette, or traditional Chinese steps to traditional Chinese music.

NARRATOR: . . . and danced and danced. It danced until much of the crop was completely trampled down . . .

   'Wheat' falls down as BEAST dances around it. Lies still.

NARRATOR: . . . and then it turned to go. Who knows where?

   Exit BEAST.

NARRATOR: In the morning Tongpo, a poor farmer, and his brother, Hong Bau, came to inspect the crops.

Enter TONGPO *and* HONG BAU. *They look amazed and anxiously inspect the flattened crop.*

TONGPO: Oh, no! The crop's been flattened!

HONG BAU: Oh good!

TONGPO: Hong Bau! What do you mean, 'Oh good!'?

HONG BAU: Well, Tongpo, we won't have to gather this part of the harvest, will we? It's hard work doing all that cutting and bending down and cutting and . . .

TONGPO: Don't be so stupid, brother! If any more of the crop is destroyed, how will we eat in winter?

HONG BAU: Oh! I hadn't thought of that.

TONGPO: No, you hadn't! I have to do the thinking for both of us.

HONG BAU *looks upset.* TONGPO *smiles.*

TONGPO: But I don't mind, brother, you're family, and my brains and your strong arm makes us a winning team, eh?

HONG BAU *nods and smiles, flexing his biceps.*

TONGPO: But we'll have to tell the village about this, and they won't like it. I wonder what could have done this damage?

HONG BAU *looks around the floor, then notices something.*

HONG BAU: Look! Animal tracks! Big ones!

TONGPO: Hey, you're right! And I hate to think what kind of beast could have made those tracks. They're enormous!

Turns to audience and picks up a large black cut-out footprint.

TONGPO: Look!

Puts footprint into his pocket.

HONG BAU: What did you do that for?
TONGPO: I'm going to take it back to the village so that we can show them what's afoot.
HONG BAU: What is afoot, then?
TONGPO: About twelve inches!
HONG BAU: Eh?

He scratches his head.

HONG BAU: I don't understand you half of the time.

TONGPO *smiles.*

TONGPO: No, you don't, do you? Come on! We'll have to run back with the news!

Runs off-stage. HONG BAU *stands, still looking puzzled, until he realises that* TONGPO *has gone.*

HONG BAU: Hey, wait for me!

Exit, running. All the 'harvest' now gets up and sits in a semi-circle facing the audience with TO MA TO *in the middle ready for Scene Two.*

Scene 2

The village. Enter NARRATOR.

NARRATOR: And so, as Tongpo is on his way to tell his friends the news, the head of the village, To Ma To, has gathered all the villagers together to discuss matters of trade etc. . . .

NARRATOR *stands to one side. The scene begins. As* TO MA TO *speaks, the villagers yawn and look bored.*

TO MA TO: And so, to conclude our monthly financial report, it only remains for me to say –

MU MU *wakes up from sleep*.

MU MU: Wha – huh – has he finished?

POH TEE: No, Mu Mu, he's only been speaking for three hours.

RATTAN: This is worse than when we were at school.

POH TEE: Yeah! Remember that silly old English teacher who used to drone on –

MU MU: I know – Bo Ring! That was his name. I've had toothaches that were more interesting than his lessons.

TO MA TO: Ahem! If I might finish . . .?

ALL: S'pose so.
     Go on, then.
     Aw, boring old duffer!
     Get it over with.
     etc., etc.

TO MA TO: Thank you. Now, where was I?

MU MU (*to the rest*): I know where he should be!

Laughter.

TO MA TO: Did you say something?

MU MU: I said I know how poor we could be if it wasn't for you, To Ma To, honourable head of this village.

TO MA TO: Yes, well, it's true. A few more bumper harvests and I – I mean *we* – will all be wealthy. Now I have this nice little insurance policy which I am sure will interest you all, and it only costs a few hundred bucks each.

They are interrupted by TONGPO *followed by* HONG BAU, *who run in excitedly.*

TONGPO (*breathlessly*): Listen everybody! Terrible news!

MU MU: They've raised the school leaving age to twenty-five?

HONG BAU: Have they really?

TONGPO: No – it's our crops.

TO MA TO: My crops? I mean, *our* crops? What's happened to them, Tongpo?

TONGPO: They've been flattened!

ALL: Flattened?

TONGPO: Yes – flattened, or at least part of them have been.

TO MA TO: Tongpo, how did this happen?

TONGPO: I think a wild beast is responsible.

TO MA TO: How do you know?

TONGPO (*pulls out footprint*): Because I found this!

First four notes of 'Dragnet' theme are heard. General shock and amazement registered by everybody.

ALL: It's huge!
        Enormous!
        Gigantic!
        Terrifying!

POH TEE: What is it?

MU MU: I wondered where my ballet instructor had got to last night!

TO MA TO: What do you think it is, Tongpo?

TONGPO: I don't know, but whatever it is, it's big and probably dangerous.

MU MU: I told you it was my ballet instructor!

TO MA TO: Well, everybody, what should we do about this dreadful creature? We'll have to do something! Any ideas?

MA CHO: I, Ma Cho, bravest and strongest warrior in the village, will fight this beast alone!

He performs some impromptu martial arts movements.

ALL: Sit down!
  He thinks he's Bruce Lee.
  Rambo!
  He-man!
  Silly old fool!

TO MA TO: This isn't like the comics you read, Ma Cho;
  you can't fight a beast that size alone.

MA CHO: Can't I?

ALL: No!

MA CHO: Then I'll take my good friend, my next-door
  neighbour – Run Wai! He'll help me to kill this beast.

   RUN WAI *looks alarmed, and everybody laughs.*

RUN WAI: I d–don't think that's a g–good idea.

MA CHO: Nonsense! We'll be heroes!

   While this is going on, MU MU *puts his hand to his mouth
   and signals everybody to be quiet. He creeps up behind* RUN
   WAI.

RUN WAI: C–can't we j–just leave it alone? Perhaps it will
  g–go away?

MU MU (*loudly from behind* RUN WAI): BOO!!

   RUN WAI *screams in terror and jumps into* MA CHO's
   arms. General laughter.

TO MA TO: No, I think we had better try something else.
  Any other ideas?

FAN TONG: I know what we should do!

ALL: Yes?

FAN TONG: First, we'll *track* the beast!

ALL: Yes!

FAN TONG: Then we'll *trap* the beast!

ALL (*enthusiastically*): Yes!!

FAN TONG: Then we'll *kill* the beast!

ALL (*excitedly*): Yes!!!

FAN TONG: Then we'll *eat* the beast!

ALL: Ye-*No*! Yuck! Bleh!

    She's food crazy!

    Bonkers!

    Bananas!

    etc., etc.

FAN TONG (*becoming more uncertain with each suggestion*):
    We can curry it! Make soup! Sandwiches? . . . Pies . . .?

    She is booed down

TO MA TO: Listen everybody! We must do something!
    Tongpo, what do you suggest?

TONGPO: Well, I think Fan Tong was right with one
    thing.

ALL: That silly old fool?

    Old greedy-guts?

    What?

    etc., etc.

TONGPO: Yes, she said we ought to trap the beast. I think
    she's right – let's build a trap! Once we've caught it we
    can decide what to do with it!

TO MA TO: Tongpo's right, but who will build this trap?

RATTAN: I might have guessed this would mean extra
    work for somebody.

MU MU: Ah, Rattan! You've woken up! Are you afraid
    someone might make you do something for a change?

RATTAN: Bah! You joker! Who are you to talk? What
    good have your useless attempts at carpentry done? Call
    yourself a village carpenter? Ha!

POH TEE: Now come on you two – stop arguing.

ALL: Yes!

    Stop it!

    etc., etc.

HONG BAU: How about you, Poh Tee, our village potter?
    Could you build us a trap?

POH TEE (*standing up*): Ah, yes! And what a creation I would make – I, Poh Tee, potter, craftsman, artist, *genius*!

He tosses back his hair in an 'artistic' pose.

POH TEE: I can see it now – people for miles around would flock to see my masterpiece; I would use subtle shades of blue and pastel pinks . . .

ALL: Oh, no!
He's off again!
Picasso!
Leonardo!

MU MU: He's got a mind just like his pots.

POH TEE: Brilliant?

MU MU: No – cracked!

General laughter.

POH TEE (*sitting down in a huff*): Peasants!

HONG BAU: What about you, Mu Mu? Couldn't you build us a trap made of wood?

MU MU: Yes, I could! 'Wooden' that be clever!

TO MA TO: Oh, no! Not his wood puns again!

MU MU (*getting quite carried away*): When we catch the beast should we let it 'pine' away? Would that be 'oak' – ay? Do you 'cedar' advantages?

MA CHO (*loudly to himself*): If he doesn't stop I'm going to 'box' his ears!

MU MU: It's about time my business 'branched' out . . . Do you get it? Have you 'twigged'?

RATTAN: You're hopeless! You'd never be able to finish on time.

MU MU: Oh yeah? Why not?

RATTAN: Because you're thick as two short 'planks'!

TONGPO: I'm sorry, Mu Mu, there isn't enough time for you to make a trap if we are to catch the beast tonight.

MU MU: Well, who else can make a trap in time?

They all look at RATTAN.

RATTAN: Oh no! Not me! Make your own trap. What do
   I care if your crops get flattened? I'm not a farmer.
TONGPO: No, but what do farmers store their seeds in
   after the harvests?
RATTAN: Why, my baskets, of course!
TONGPO: And who will buy your baskets if there are no
   crops?
RATTAN: Er – well – let me see . . .
TONGPO: Well, Rattan?
RATTAN (*feebly*): Nobody.
TONGPO: I beg your pardon, Rattan, I didn't quite hear
   that – what was that again?
RATTAN (*shouting*): Nobody! Nobody will buy them, so I
   suppose I'd better make your rotten trap. I dunno, it's
   always me who gets the worst jobs.

   They all humour her and slap her on the back.

TO MA TO: Right then, let's help her. Come everybody!
   My – I mean *our* – crops must be saved!

   Exit ALL, *humouring a complaining* RATTAN; *and enter*
   NARRATOR.

NARRATOR: And so they set about making the trap.

   Loud bangings heard offstage.

NARRATOR: Rattan and Mu Mu put the final finishing
   touches to their creation.

   NARRATOR *stands to one side. Enter* RATTAN *and*
   MU MU *carrying a large basket. It need not look too much like
   a trap. They are also carrying hammers, saws etc.*

MU MU: Well, I never thought you had it in you.

RATTAN (*smiling*): So you admit that my work is top quality?

MU MU: No, I've just said I never did think you had it in you. Now I'm positive.

RATTAN: Why you! (*Raises her hand*)

MU MU: No, I don't mean it – really it's very good – after all, I did help you. Well done!

RATTAN *smiles.*

MU MU (*aside*): At least, my part was well done!

Enter POH TEE. *He stops to look at the trap, using his hands in the way artists do, to size it up.*

POH TEE: Ah, yes. I see it all.

RATTAN: What are you talking about, jughead?

POH TEE: What you need is a few finishing touches.

MU MU (*raising hammer*): Funny you should say that, I was about to say the same to you.

POH TEE: A sensitive application of colour; a few touches of indigo here . . . (*He points to opening of trap.*)

RATTAN: Indigo where?

MU MU: Indigo here . . . and out dey go dere!

POH TEE: . . . a hint of pink there and a dash of mauve . . . there! Ah, yes; once I've finished with it, it will be the talk of the province. 'Painted Trap' by Poh Tee, genius. (*He brushes his hair back and touches his brow.*)

RATTAN: He's off again. Hey, clear off, Picasso; this is a trap, not a work of art!

POH TEE: Peasants!

Exit POH TEE.

MU MU: Come on, Rattan, keep your trap shut.

RATTAN (*raising her hammer*): What did you say?

MU MU: Your trap – you've left it open!

RATTAN: Oh. Okay, let's go.

They exit, MU MU winking at the audience as they go.

Scene 3

The fields. Enter NARRATOR, *stands centre stage.*
VILLAGERS *stand as before, in mime of the crop.*

NARRATOR: That night the beast came once more, dancing and trampling over the crops.

> *Enter* BEAST, *dancing as before; crop is trampled as before.*

NARRATOR: When the beast saw the trap, it gave one swipe of its mighty paw and destroyed it.

> BEAST *playfully kicks the trap aside. Exit, followed by the 'crop'.*

NARRATOR: And so, the next morning, the villagers, led by Tongpo, went to see if their trap had worked.

> NARRATOR *steps to one side. Enter* VILLAGERS.

TONGPO: Right – here goes, everybody; let's see if we've caught the beast.

> *They tip-toe towards the trap.* TONGPO *looks in carefully, then stands back wearily.*

TONGPO: It's no use; it hasn't worked. The beast has broken the trap like paper.
ALL: Oh no! (*etc.*)
MU MU: This is all Rattan's fault for building a rubbishy trap.
RATTAN: What!
MU MU: Perhaps if we show it your ugly face instead it would scare the beast away!
RATTAN: Why, you splinter-brained blockhead! I'll nail you right now!

The others restrain RATTAN *as she charges towards* MU MU.

TONGPO: Hey, hold it, you guys! Mu Mu has just given me an idea!

MU MU: Yeah! Rattan's face would scare anybody!

TONGPO: No, I don't mean that. But what if we did scare the beast away?

TO MA TO: How do we do that, Tongpo?

TONGPO: We'll make a beast of our own, fierce enough to scare it away. But first of all we do this – gather round, everybody!

They ALL *put their heads together in a whispered conference.* NARRATOR *goes centre stage.*

NARRATOR: And so it was decided. Tongpo and Hong Bau were to stay in the fields that night to observe the beast, so that they might know what kind of creature they had to face.

VILLAGERS *stand in 'crop' formation.* TONGPO *and* HONG BAU *creep in from the side of the stage.* NARRATOR *waits at other side, still in view of the audience.*

HONG BAU: Sshhh!

TONGPO: But I'm not saying anything!

HONG BAU: But you said something just now!

TONGPO: I wouldn't have said anything if you hadn't said 'sshhh'.

HONG BAU: Sshhh!

TONGPO (*to audience, in stage whisper*): Oh, I give up! (*to* HONG BAU) Look, let's hide over there until the beast or whatever it is turns up.

HONG BAU: Okay.

They hide at the side of the stage but still in view of audience.

NARRATOR (*loudly*): And so Tongpo and Hong Bau –

TONGPO: ⎫

HONG BAU: ⎰ Sshhh!

NARRATOR: Oh yes . . . Ahem! (*more quietly now*) And so Tongpo and Hong Bau waited in fear for the beast to arrive.

TONGPO: Hey! We're not afraid!

NARRATOR (*looking annoyed*): Who's telling this story? Oh, all right then. 'And so Tongpo and Hong Bau waited *bravely* for the beast to arrive'. Better?

TONGPO: Thank you.

NARRATOR: Right then, we'll continue . . . When the full moon was at its height the fearful beast arrived . . .

Enter BEAST *as before, dancing either to a) pop music or b) traditional Chinese music.*

NARRATOR: . . . and began once again to dance amongst the crops.

HONG BAU: Oh no! It's awful!

[OPTION: *the following section can be added if pop music is being used.*

　　HONG BAU: *has his eyes shut tight and his fingers in his ears.*

TONGPO: The beast?

HONG BAU: No – the music! I hate the Rolling Stones! (*or whatever*)

　　HONG BAU: *opens his eyes.*

HONG BAU: Oh no! Is that the beast? That's even worse! Aagh!]

TONGPO: So fierce-looking!

HONG BAU: And look what it's doing to our crops!

BEAST flattens crops as before and exits.

TONGPO: Come on! Let's tell the others!

Exit TONGPO and HONG BAU. NARRATOR goes centre stage.

NARRATOR: And so, having learned about the beast's fierce appearance the villagers make a beast of their own.

NARRATOR steps to one side. Enter VILLAGERS, carrying pots, pans, gongs and a lion dance outfit.

TONGPO (*carrying head of lion dance outfit*): Right then, we follow our plan! I'll put on this mask and be the head and Hong Bau will go behind and be the body. As soon as the beast appears, the rest of you make as much noise as you can with your pots and pans. Then we'll see how fierce this beast really is! (*Aside, to HONG BAU*) I hope our plan works, or we're in big trouble.

HONG BAU: Don't worry, brother; have faith.

TONGPO: Right everybody – the moon has risen; if the beast does the same as last night it should be here by now. Keep quiet!

Enter BEAST, as before. It looks arond for crops, finds none, and looks away from the VILLAGERS.

TONGPO: NOW!

VILLAGERS advance slowly, banging their pots and pans. The BEAST runs around in confused circles. Then TONGPO and HONG BAU step forward in their lion dance outfit. The BEAST turns around, sees them, jumps into the air and runs away. Exit BEAST.

ALL: Hooray!

TONGPO *and* HONG BAU *take off their disguise and are carried off on the shoulders of the grateful* VILLAGERS. NARRATOR *steps forward; as he is speaking the* VILLAGERS *re-enter and line up before the audience, hands joined.*

NARRATOR: Ever since that time, Chinese people the world over celebrate Chinese New Year by dancing in an animal mask which they call 'The Lucky Lion'. They wish each other a happy and prosperous New Year – or, to put it in the Chinese:

ALL: GONG XI FA CAI!

All bow and exit.

[*Curtain*]

Wishful Thinking

CHARACTERS

DESMOND, *a teenage schoolboy*
HIS MOTHER
HIS TEACHER
SALLY, *a teenage schoolgirl*
TOUT
GENIE
PASSING STRANGER
POLICE CONSTABLE

SCENE: A city street
Properties
One packet of cigarettes (preferably fake!)
One pipe
One briefcase/suitcase with stand
Several cigarette lighters
Dead leaves (cut-up brown paper would do)
Paste jewellery/diamond necklace (coloured foil would do)
One shoelace
Background scenery for a busy street

Scene 1

A busy street on a Saturday morning. Enter DESMOND. *He is fashionably dressed and smoking a cigarette.*

DESMOND (*to audience*): Hi there! (*He takes a drag at his cigarette and coughs. He delivers the next lines in the form of a 'rap'.*)

> This is the life! It's the weekend,
> Saturday morning, money to spend!
> Homework done, ain't no school –
> Feeling good, and (*Breaks off to cough violently.*
> Then, feebly*) – looking cool . . .?

Enter SALLY.

SALLY: 'Morning, Desmond!

DESMOND: Wotcha, Sally!

SALLY: I thought you were giving up those stupid fags, Des.

DESMOND: Yeah, well, one does what one must to look cool and crucial . . . and fags are definitely in.

SALLY: Not according to me! If we'd been meant to smoke we'd've been born with chimneys on our heads! Talk about having money to burn . . . yours is going up in smoke for a start. (*She giggles.*)

DESMOND (*offended*): Thanks for the sermon, Sally. But I can spend my money how I like.

SALLY: Pardon me! Anyway, aren't you supposed to have a Saturday job?

DESMOND: I did have but I've promised to help Mum out in the shop on Saturdays, starting next week, so I packed my job in today. And that means that now, my dear, I am a wealthy young dude with time on my hands!

SALLY: Coo – get you, Mr Smoothy! But what would your Mum say about your smoking?

DESMOND (*to audience, as he puts out his cigarette*): She's right, you know – my Mum would be really disappointed if she could see me flashing these gaspers. But I just can't seem to break the habit! And there's my teacher an' all – take yesterday, for instance . . .

DESMOND *and* SALLY *move centre stage to the rear.* DESMOND's MOTHER *enters and stands stage right; she has a cigarette hanging from her mouth for the duration. His* TEACHER, *wearing a tweed jacket and smoking a pipe, enters and stands stage left. They speak both to* DESMOND *and to the audience.*

TEACHER: Smoking again, Desmond? What would your mother think?

MOTHER: Aw, Desmond, you're too young to smoke! (*Takes a long drag*)

TEACHER (*poking his pipe accusingly in* DESMOND's *direction*): I'd have thought a bright lad like you could have more sense.

MOTHER: Fags are a waste of your job money – and you know every penny counts since your Dad's been gone!

TEACHER: And you're not doing too well at school either – but I know you could if you'd only try!

MOTHER: Try to set a good example to your little brother, Des, try to help me out in the shop – make me proud, Des, don't let me down!

TEACHER: Don't let us down, Desmond. Make us proud!

Here on TEACHER *and* MOTHER *break into a 'rap'.*

TEACHER: ⎫ MOTHER: ⎭	Make us proud, don't let us down!
TEACHER:	Don't be a failure in this town!
TEACHER: ⎫ MOTHER: ⎭	Don't let us down, make us proud!
MOTHER:	But smokin', Desmond, ain't allowed.

TEACHER: ⎱ (*as they exit*):
MOTHER   ⎰ Make us proud, don't let us down!

> *Repeat and fade as they exit, wagging pipe/cigarette.*
> DESMOND *and* SALLY *move centre stage again.*

DESMOND (*to audience*): Well, something like that anyway
– know what I mean? But even though I know really that
it's a waste of time and money I can't stop! Besides, the
grown-ups smoke, don't they? Personally I think it makes
me look more adult . . . (*takes another drag and coughs*) . . .
and sophisticated.

SALLY: Gor blimey, Des; get much more sophisticated and
you'll end up in hospital!

> *Enter a* TOUT *with a briefcase which he opens and places
> on a folding stand to make a little display.*

SALLY: Who's this then?

TOUT (*loudly, in barrow-boy manner*): Come and get your
cigarette lighters, all shiny and new, just in time for
Christmas! A perfect gift for your friends and family! All
the best in designer names – Monex, Rumhill, Yves St
Louis, Davini . . .

DESMOND (*interested*): Lighters?

TOUT: . . . all genuine! Only a pound a throw, ladies and
gentlemen, only a pound!

DESMOND: Hey!

TOUT: Yes, sir? You have a lucky face – be my first
customer and you can have one for only ninety-five 'p'!

DESMOND: Ninety-five pence? I thought you said they
were genuine? They can't be at that price!

TOUT: Genuine? Yessir, all guaranteed genuine copies –
can't tell 'em apart from the real things, which I may say
cost a fortune!

SALLY: Aw, Des, don't waste your money!

DESMOND: Hang on . . . Davini, you said . . .?

TOUT: Yessir – even Davini himself couldn't tell the difference!

DESMOND: Right – I'll take one!

SALLY: Like I said – money to burn!

TOUT: Right you are, sir! (*Sells* DESMOND *the lighter*) And your change – ta!

SALLY: Isn't this illegal? Shall I ask that policeman over there?

TOUT: Policeman? What policeman? (*Quickly packs up*) Well, must be off – ta-ta!

Exit TOUT *in a hurry.*

SALLY (*laughing*): Look at him go – whoosh!

DESMOND (*not noticing*): Cor! Just like a real Davini! Think I'll try it out! (*Takes out another cigarette*)

SALLY: Aw, Des, not another one!

DESMOND (*putting cigarette into his mouth, trying to look like James Bond*): '. . . and so the suave man-of-the-world relaxes with his mentholated cigarette . . .'

DESMOND *flicks the lighter but never gets to light his cigarette, because he is interrupted by the entrance of the* GENIE. *The* GENIE *can be announced by e.g. a clash of cymbals or a roll of drums. The* GENIE *is larger than* DESMOND *and is wearing a gangster-type pinstripe suit and dark glasses. He approaches* DESMOND *from behind so although* DESMOND *is looking around for the source of the unexpected noise he doesn't notice the* GENIE *at first.*

SALLY: Des – look out!

GENIE *taps* DESMOND *on the shoulder.*

DESMOND (*startled*): Ah!

GENIE (*in a voice like a Mafia gangster – an Italian 'Godfather' accent would be appropriate*): Ey, whaddya call me for, eh?

DESMOND: Sorry, officer, I didn't know they were copies – I was just going to report that tout anyway.

GENIE: I ain't no police officer, dopeface.

DESMOND: Wh-who are you, then?

GENIE: Ey, the Genie of the Lighter! (*Glancing at the audience and tapping his head*) What else, eh?

SALLY (*glancing at the audience and tapping her head*): Des, he's a nutter. Let's go.

DESMOND (*edging nervously away*): Well – er – it's been very nice meeting you, sir . . . I'll just be on my way.

DESMOND *turns to go. The* GENIE *detains him with a firm hold on his shoulder.*

GENIE: Hold it, kiddo! I can't let you go, not until –

DESMOND (*shouting in alarm*): Help! I'm being mugged! Help, police, poli –

DESMOND's *cries cease abruptly as the* GENIE *waves his hands dramatically.* DESMOND *continues to open and shut his mouth soundlessly, like a stranded fish, but to no avail. His voice has been taken away and he has been frozen to the spot.*

GENIE: That's better. I can't let you go, kid, until I fulfil my obligation to you.

SALLY: You brute! (*She kicks the* GENIE *on the shin but he merely smiles.*) Help!

Enter a passing STRANGER. SALLY *rushes up to him.*

SALLY: Help – stop him – he's attacking Desmond.

STRANGER (*obviously unable to see the* GENIE): Who is?

SALLY (*pointing to smiling* GENIE): He is! Stop him, quick!

STRANGER (*looking puzzled*): There ain't no-one there! 'Ere . . . (*suddenly smiling*) . . . you're from the telly, ain't you? That show with the hidden cameras?

SALLY: Oh please! Help!

STRANGER (*waving and looking around*): Hello, Mum!
(*Peers around*) Clever how they hide these cameras!

SALLY: Can't you see him? Stop him!

STRANGER: Stop him? (*Laughing*) Yeah, I'll stop him! I'll
just get my ray-gun from my space-ship first. Tara!

Exit passing STRANGER *still waving Hello to Mum.*

GENIE: It's-a no good. They can't see me. Only you two
can see me. Now you gonna listen?

DESMOND *nods dumbly but violently.*

GENIE (*to* SALLY): And you?

SALLY (*sulkily*): Got no choice, have I?

GENIE: No. (*He waves his hand and* DESMOND *is restored.*)
Now, where was I?

DESMOND: How did you do that? And who are you,
anyway?

SALLY: Des, he's just a nutter! A looney – two bricks short
of a load!

GENIE: Hey, you were gonna listen, not talk, remember?
Now shaddup!

DESMOND: Oh, never mind her! Carry on! (*To* SALLY,
in a stage whisper) Be quiet and humour him!

GENIE: Thank you. Well, I suppose you know the story of
Aladdin and his Wonderful Lamp?

DESMOND: Of course!

SALLY: Yeah – saw the panto when I was a kid.

GENIE: Well, that's me. The Genie of Aladdin's Wonderful
Lamp.

SALLY: So that's it! You're a loony actor!

GENIE (*angrily*): No, stupid! I'm-a no actor; I'm-a the real
thing!

DESMOND (*laughing*): Oh yeah? And I'm the King of the
Fairies!

GENIE: No you ain't. I had lunch with him last week.

SALLY (*to* DESMOND): I told you he was loony, Des! (*To*
    GENIE) Look, whoever you are, say what you have to
    say and then go, please!

GENIE: I think maybe you need a little more persuasion,
    eh? Whaddya have in your pockets?

DESMOND: Oh, I get it – you are a mugger after all!

GENIE (*raising his voice*): Ey! Whaddya have in your
    pockets? Take a look!

DESMOND: Okay, okay! Don't get mad! (*He puts his hands
    into his pockets.*)

SALLY (*to* DESMOND): He already is, Des – mad as a
    hatter!

DESMOND (*to* GENIE): Look . . . just a few coins, see?

He opens his hands to show the GENIE, *and the audience, a
handful of bright jewels.* DESMOND *himself is watching the*
GENIE's *face and does not see.*

DESMOND (*looking down at his hands*): Hey! Where'd they
    come from? They're jewels! What about you, Sal – what
    have you got?

SALLY: Oh, that's just an old trick – any kids' magician
    could do that!

DESMOND: Take a look in your pockets, Sal!

SALLY: All right. (*Reaches into her pockets*) But I've only got
    my old shoelace, that's all . . . (*voice tails off as she discovers
    a diamond necklace*) Wow! It looks like a diamond necklace!

GENIE: Put them back in your pockets.

They do so.

GENIE: Now empty your pockets again.

They do so: DESMOND *this time produces a handful of
dead leaves and* SALLY *produces a shoe-lace.*

DESMOND: Huh, where'd the jewels go? Where did these
    dead leaves come from?

GENIE: That'd be telling! Now for some more proof . . .

SALLY (*to* DESMOND): Proof? His party tricks don't fool me! I still think he's some nut with a screw loose!

GENIE: See that policeman heading this way?

DESMOND: } Yeah?
SALLY:

Enter POLICE CONSTABLE, *strolling nonchalantly on his beat. He stops in front of them.*

GENIE: Ask him to sing you a song.

DESMOND: Don't be daft – that's Constable Higgins! He'd think we were as nutty as y – I mean, he'd think we were crazy!

GENIE: Would he now?

Raises his hands in signal of command, and CONSTABLE HIGGINS *turns to them.*

HIGGINS: Any requests? Beatles? Elvis? Easy Listenin'?

DESMOND and SALLY begin to giggle. DESMOND plucks up the courage to ask for a request.

DESMOND: Do you know . . . (*mentions any current pop-song from the charts*)

CONSTABLE HIGGINS performs complete with pop-star mannerisms. DESMOND and SALLY stare and double-up laughing.

SALLY: My turn! My turn! Do you know my mum's favourite? (*mentions any popular ballad*)

CONSTABLE HIGGINS again obliges, in the manner of a night-club crooner. DESMOND and SALLY are delighted.

GENIE: I think that's enough!

GENIE *drops his hands;* CONSTABLE HIGGINS *stops in mid-verse and notices* DESMOND *and* SALLY *laughing.*

HIGGINS: What are you two laughing at? Not up to mischief I hope?

DESMOND: Don't worry, Constable Higgins – nothing to make a song and dance about! (*He and* SALLY *unsuccessfully try to stifle their giggles.*)

HIGGINS: Hmm . . . Well, I'll be on my way. Keep out of trouble, you two!

Exit CONSTABLE HIGGINS.

GENIE: Convinced now?

SALLY: I am!

DESMOND: Me too, that's why we didn't ask PC Plod for assistance. But I think you'd better explain, Mr – er – Mr Genie.

GENIE: You know, you remind me of Aladdin. He didn't believe me all those centuries ago, either – just like-a the others.

DESMOND: ⎱ Others?
SALLY: ⎰

GENIE: That's-a-right! After Aladdin, they all-a wanted the lamp. I tell you, it was-a Lamp-o-mania!

DESMOND: ⎱ (*blankly*): Lampomania?
SALLY: ⎰

GENIE (*firmly*): Lampomania! All-a your most-a famous types, they make it 'cos of-a *me!* Ghengis Khan, Napoleon, Mrs Thatcher –

SALLY: Mrs *Thatcher?*

GENIE (*shrugging*): Ey – we all-a make-a da mistake! Anyway, I was getting no peace at all. Everybody was after the lamp. I tell you, even genies need a rest every hundred years or so. Ah, to be 'ome with-a my mamma's spaghetti. But do I get my rest? No way!

DESMOND: Yeah, but what's all this got to do with me? I haven't got any lamp! All *I*'ve got is a lighter.

GENIE: I was coming to that, kiddo. Now, where was I? Oh yes. So I thought a change of scenery was needed. I thought if I moved out of my shabby old lamp into something modern and sophisticated – something expensive, with a bit of class – I'd get-a some respect!

DESMOND: I know what you mean.

GENIE: Anyway, yesterday I moved in thinking I'd be left safe in some shop window away from all-a the cheap peasants and greedy graspers – out of their price range. Or else bought by some spoilt rich kid who'd just throw me into the back of his mansion and leave me in – 'ow you say? – in pieces.

SALLY: Pieces?

GENIE: No, no . . . in peace, that's whadda I mean.

DESMOND: So what happened?

GENIE: Ah – I make-a da big mistake! Just when I think I got myself nice exclusive expensive designer-name cigarette lighter – a Davini – I get sold for ninety-five 'p'! The shame of it! Nobody told me about these copies!

DESMOND: No problem! You can have the lighter and clear off if it'd make you happy.

GENIE: It's not-a so simple. I was just having a nice game of bridge – my team against the Greek Gods – when what happens? You summon me up!

DESMOND: So?

GENIE: So I gotta grant you three wishes or they throw me outta the Genie's Union.

DESMOND: ⎫
SALLY: ⎬ Three wishes?

GENIE: Well, don't stand there like-a da codfish! Yeah, three and no more. So whaddya want first, eh?

SALLY: Cor – do I get three as well?

GENIE: You shaddup-a-you face. Only the boy has the lighter – only the boy has the wishes – be grateful I letta you watch.

SALLY: Pardon me for breathing!

GENIE: 'Saright. (*To* DESMOND) Well, kiddo?

DESMOND: I – I dunno . . . (*fumbles with another cigarette and raises it to his mouth*)

SALLY: Trust you, Des. When in doubt, have a snout.

DESMOND (*embarrassed*): You're right, Sal. I wish I could stop smoking.

GENIE: Your wish is granted!

DESMOND: Hey! I didn't mean –

SALLY: Des! You great plonker! Now look what you've gone and done!

DESMOND: Yeah, well . . . (*relaxes, and putting the cigarette to his mouth he raises the lighter and flicks it on*) Maybe it's not such a bad idea after all, I mean – Hey! (*as he realises what he is doing*) What's this? I was just about to smoke! (*To* GENIE) What's your game, then? How come I was just about to light up – after *you* said I could give up smoking?

GENIE: You wished you *could* stop smoking. You didn't ask-a me actually to *stop* you!

DESMOND: ⎫
SALLY: ⎬ Huh? Explain!

GENIE: If you'd told-a me you wanted to stop smoking, I could have done that easily by a-rubbin' you out –

DESMOND: Rubbin' me out . . .?

SALLY: He means killing you, Des.

GENIE: That's-a right, lady. Or I could have sealed up-a your mouth. As it is you wished you *could* stop smoking and-a you can – any time-a you want to! If you don't want to that's-a your problem. Though it seems like a waste of a perfectly good wish to me.

DESMOND: Hey, that's not fair!

GENIE (*sighing and shrugging his shoulders*): You mortals are all the same . . . you haven't a clue how to make wishes.

SALLY: How do you mean?

DESMOND: Yeah, a wish is a wish, after all.

GENIE: Ah – but you have-a to be careful how you word your wish, because I have to obey your wish to the letter, kiddo! That's the rules! Look, for example, one of my masters was-a ve-ery stupido. He asked to be covered in gold. He got his wish.

DESMOND: What's wrong with that?

GENIE: He *was* covered in gold. *Molten* gold. He's in a museum now – name of Tutankhamun – maybe you heard of him, eh?

SALLY: Ugh! How *could* you?

GENIE: Well, I was in a bad mood, see? Still, you don't appear to be as greedy as he was. What's-a the next wish? And remember – think carefully about how you ask for it!

SALLY: Yeah, Des, be careful – he's not going to do you any favours, this fella!

DESMOND: Right, let's see . . . (*to audience*) this would be a good opportunity to help my mum for a change! (*To* GENIE) Okay, Mr Genie – I wish for all my mum's money worries to disappear right now.

GENIE: Done.

SALLY: That was quick!

DESMOND: Yeah, how'd you do it?

GENIE: Easy. I burned-a your mother's shop down.

SALLY (*horrified*): Oh, no!

DESMOND: What? That's our home too!

GENIE: Yes, well, lucky for you your mother and brother weren't in it at-a the time! Oh, and she's-a been declared bankrupt too . . . and no insurance money, either.

DESMOND: Why not?

GENIE: Your mother never told you how badly she was in debt. She couldn't afford to pay the premiums any more.

DESMOND: But you've ruined her – and me! I thought you were going to make her money worries disappear!

GENIE: I told-a you to *think* about your wishes! Your mother's money worries have disappeared because she no longer has any money to worry *about*! (*Smugly*) Even her small change melted in the till.

SALLY: But she's worse off now than ever before!

GENIE: True. Her worries are about a lack of money now.

DESMOND: You're a rotten twister!

SALLY: You're horrible!

GENIE (*casually examining his fingernails*): I told-a you I could be in a bad mood. You'd better not mess up-a the next wish, kiddo. It's your last one!

SALLY: Des – you've had two wishes already, and they've brought nothing but trouble – think carefully, Des! *Think!*

> DESMOND *sits down on a doorstep with his head in his hands.*

DESMOND (*to audience*): They're right . . . what can I do to put things straight? This is my last wish, so I'll have to think very carefully, I daren't mess this up! What on earth can I ask for that this crafty Genie can't turn against me?

> *What is Desmond to do? It's up to you! Finish the play yourselves. You must find a way of wording the last wish so that the Genie cannot turn it against Desmond. What should he ask for? Think carefully about each possibility before you decide – then write the script, and perform the play!*

How to Steal a Troll's Trombone

CHARACTERS

WHITE KNIGHT
TROLL

SCENE: A forest

Properties
One trombone
One branch of wood
One pair of handcuffs
One piece of rope
Armour for the knight (excluding sword)
Backdrops representing trees

The forest. Enter WHITE KNIGHT, *a prim-looking nobleman with no sword. He whistles a bit, when all of a sudden the* TROLL *jumps up in front of him, a fearsome creature, roaring horribly, carrying a trombone.*

TROLL: A-ha! Now, 'brave' Knight, take out your sword and meet your doom, for I, the Troll of the Forest, shall bash you and mince you and leave your remains for my crows to eat!

Pause. WHITE KNIGHT *looks slowly at fuming* TROLL.

KNIGHT: Shan't.

Pause. TROLL *is confused.*

TROLL (*roaring*): Oh, but you shall, you vermin! Try to steal my magic trombone, would you? The one that can charm gold from the sky with its music. I'll teach you, you scum. Defend yourself!

TROLL *lays down the trombone and adopts a boxing stance. There is a pause.* KNIGHT *looks unconcernedly at the* TROLL.

KNIGHT: Shan't.

KNIGHT *sits down cross-legged on the floor. Another pause.* TROLL *is amazed. He begins ranting again.*

TROLL: You chicken-livered coward! Have you no fight in you? Pick up your sword and fight . . . Oh! I see! You have no sword! Well, I'm not an unreasonable Troll. I don't expect you to fight a great big strong troll like me without a weapon of some sort. Here –

TROLL *throws* KNIGHT *a hefty branch from the ground.*

TROLL: – use this. Now fight!

Adopts boxing stance once more. KNIGHT *looks at branch, looks at* TROLL, *then shifts around making himself more comfortable.*

KNIGHT: Shan't.

Another pause.

TROLL: But you've got to!
KNIGHT: Shan't.

Another pause.

TROLL: Knights are supposed to fight Trolls. It's in the rules. A knight comes along, tries to steal my trombone, I clobber him, then wait for the next knight. Now what could be more simple than that? . . . Now fight!
KNIGHT: Shan't.

TROLL *scratches his head, thoroughly puzzled.*

TROLL: Oh, all right then! I'll fight you with one hand behind my back, seeing as you're such a scrawny knight!

Puts one hand behind his back.

TROLL: Come on!

TROLL *bounces around shaking his free fist.*

KNIGHT (*looking indifferently at* TROLL): Shan't.
TROLL: Is there no satisfying you? Look, I'll tell you what I'll do. I'll put handcuffs on – look, here!

TROLL *puts on handcuffs.*

TROLL: I'll even throw away the key!

Does so.

TROLL: You can fight me now!
KNIGHT: Shan't.

TROLL (*thoroughly exasperated*): Aagh-h! I'll tie my feet up as well . . .

Does so, and promptly tumbles over.

TROLL: . . . and look, I'm even lying down on the floor! Now will you fight, you miserable, cowardly wretch?

KNIGHT gets up, brushing himself down fastidiously, and languidly picks up the branch. He raises it as if to strike the TROLL, then pauses, looking consideringly at the TROLL with his head on one side. Then he smiles, tosses the branch away, pats the TROLL condescendingly on the head, and picks up the Trombone instead. He begins to stroll away.

TROLL: Hey! Hey, come back!

TROLL struggles to stand up and follow, but keeps falling over.

TROLL: Hey! You tricked me, you miserable . . . Give me back my magic trombone!

KNIGHT pauses at the point of going off-stage.

KNIGHT (*smugly*): Shan't.

[*Curtain*]

Benny and the Woodwose

CHARACTERS

Convicts
NOSHER (*the big one*)
SID (*the little one*)

Teachers
MR COOPER (*'Sir'*)
MRS COOPER (*'Miss'*)

Boy Scouts
Scout 1 (BENNY)
Scout 2 (CRAIG)
Scout 3 (JULIAN)
Scout 4 (ROYSTON)

Girl Guides
Guide 1 (TRACY)
Guide 2 (JUDY)
Guide 3 (AVRIL)
Guide 4 (PAULA)

Policemen
POLICEMAN 1
POLICEMAN 2

SCENE: A forest campsite

Properties
Two handguns
Logs of various sizes
Camp stools
Rope
Knapsacks containing food, money, clothing
Book with title 'HYPNOTISM' on the cover in large letters

Pocket-watch on a chain
Soft-drink tins
Forest backdrops

Scene 1

A forest clearing. Shots are heard. Enter NOSHER *and* SID, *in convict uniforms and short of breath.*

NOSHER: Stand still!
SID: Are they gone, Nosher?
NOSHER: Quiet, Sid!

    NOSHER *listens. Shots are fainter.*

NOSHER: Yeah! Heh, heh! I think we've shaken them off at last!
SID: What do we do now, Nosher?
NOSHER: We've got to get as far away from those police and prison guards as possible if we want to make good our escape.
SID: One of them nearly got us, Nosher – I wonder what happened to him?
NOSHER: He was – shall we say – unavoidably detained.
SID: Oh! I see . . . I think. What now, Nosher?
NOSHER: We've got to find food, my little friend, so we'll have to find some people who will very kindly give us some.
SID: D'you think they will, Nosher?
NOSHER: I think they will, Sid.
SID: How do you know, Nosher?
NOSHER: 'Cos I'll be asking them with this! (*Pulls out a pistol*) Courtesy of our policeman friend, who now sleeps the sleep of the innocent. Come on, Sid – let's go. (*Puts the pistol away.*)
SID: N–Nosher . . .
NOSHER: What?
SID: I'm afraid.
NOSHER: You're always afraid, Sid.

SID: I mean, of the forest – there's terrible things in the forest, Nosher, terrible. I've heard of things that would make your blood run cold.

NOSHER: Well, if we don't want our blood to run cold we'd better find some food! Now follow me!

SID (*looking nervously right and left*): R-right, Nosher, w-whatever you s-say.

   Exit.

Scene 2

A forest clearing. Enter SIR *and* MISS *leading* SCOUTS *and* GUIDES *marching in neat lines, except for* BENNY *and* TRACY *who slouch and do not sing. The rest are singing 'Ten Green Bottles'.*

ALL: '. . . and if one green bottle should accidentally fall, there'd be no green bottles hanging on the wall.'

   Laughter.

MR COOPER: Right, everybody, that was a good day's hiking. Let's camp here for the night.

   They all sit down, have drinks etc. BENNY *and* TRACY *sit forward, nearest the audience.*

BENNY (*groans*): That was at least fifty miles! Oh, my poor feet! (*He rubs his feet.*)

TRACY: We must have got through about a thousand bottles hanging from that wall. (*Opens a cola can and drinks some.*)

BENNY: Yeah, if I hear that song again, I'll go crackers. (*Looks thirstily at the cola can.*) Thirsty work, walking. And singing.

TRACY: Want a cola? (*Offers him another can.*)

BENNY: Yeah, thanks! (*Accepts can, opens it hurriedly, drinks it noisily.*) Whew! That was needed.

TRACY: Didn't you bring a drink, then?

BENNY: Nah!

TRACY: Why not?

BENNY: 'Cos you had one for me!

TRACY: I might not have had!

BENNY: But you did have – you, or somebody else would have had one.

TRACY: Benny!

BENNY: I'm right, though, aren't I, Tracy? There's always somebody so why should I bother to stock up and burden myself? See (*he shows her his pack*) – my pack's half the weight of anybody else's.

TRACY: So's your brain from the sound of things. What'd you come on this walk for if you hate the scouts so much?

BENNY: My Dad. He says I think too much about my own satisfaction and not enough about other people's. (*Adopts a mocking voice.*) 'My son, you will never truly value yourself unless you first value others.' Who does he think he is – Cliff Richard?

TRACY: Yeah, my mum's the same.

BENNY: This is another of his efforts to make me 'grow up' as he calls it. He keeps on about learning to trust others. Well, I do trust them – trust them to provide me with what I want, when I want it!

TRACY: Yeah, but what if I'd been the one with no cola to drink – what then?

BENNY: But you did have.

TRACY: But if I hadn't.

BENNY: As I said – there'd be somebody else. (*Sees CRAIG and PAULA approaching, apparently absorbed in some rope in CRAIG's hands.*) Look, I'll show you. (*To CRAIG and PAULA*). Hi.

CRAIG: Hi, Benny!

PAULA: Hi!

BENNY: What're you doing?

CRAIG: We're practising tying knots. I'm showing Paula how to tie a reef knot.

PAULA: And Craig's been showing me how to tie a clove-hitch.

BENNY: That's fascinating.

CRAIG: Yes – we're helping each other study for our advanced knot-tying course. If we can fasten thirty knots we get a badge.

PAULA (*nodding enthusiastically*): Yes, and then we get a better chance of going on next term's mountaineering course!

BENNY: A badge, eh?

CRAIG: ⎫
PAULA: ⎬ Yes!

BENNY: With a motto?

CRAIG: Yes!

PAULA: The motto is 'Always Secure' for the knots badge.

CRAIG: And 'In Each Other We Trust' for the mountaineering badge. I hope we can get one of those, too!

BENNY: That's really nice.

CRAIG: ⎫
PAULA: ⎬ Yes!

BENNY: By the way –

CRAIG: ⎫
PAULA: ⎬ Yes?

BENNY: Would you happen to have a spare cola on you?

PAULA: Sorry, Benny. We only carry water on hikes. Don't you know soft drinks are not very good for a real thirst? Too much sugar.

BENNY: Is that so?

CRAIG: Paula's right, but you're welcome to some of our water.

BENNY: Er – no, thanks.

CRAIG: Hey, would you like to help with some of our knots?

BENNY: Not just now – I'm a bit, er, tied up at the moment.

TRACY *groans*.

PAULA: See you later, then . . .

CRAIG: . . . round the camp fire tonight. 'Bye!

Exit CRAIG *and* PAULA.

TRACY: You were saying . . .?

BENNY: Huh! I wish those two would get knotted!

TRACY: You didn't get your cola.

BENNY: Yeah, but they did offer me water, and that's a drink.

TRACY *laughs*.

BENNY: Well, it's true! (*Pause.*) People like that make me sick, always working together, insisting on being in a team like a lot of ants. Where's their sense of independence, their individuality?

TRACY: Like you have, you mean?

BENNY: Yeah! Just like me. I don't need any stupid team – I'm a one-man show, a class act all by myself!

TRACY: Yeah?

BENNY: Yeah!

TRACY: We'll see.

Scene 3

The camp fire at night. Enter MRS COOPER *and* JUDY. *The other guides and Julian are already seated around the fire.*

MRS COOPER: Now settle down, everybody. (*To* JUDY, *in a kindly voice*) Don't worry, there are no dangerous animals in there, you're completely safe.

JUDY: Sorry, Miss. I just thought I heard a sound. It won't happen again, Miss.

An owl screeches.

JUDY (*alarmed*): What's that?

TRACY: Oh, be quiet!

MRS COOPER: It's only an owl, dear. Now just sit here, next to Julian and Avril.

JULIAN: Don't worry, Judy. We'll protect you, won't we, Avril?

AVRIL: You bet.

TRACY: Yeah, but who'll protect her from you two?

Laughter. Enter MR COOPER *with the scouts.*

MR COOPER (*sounding jolly*): Sit down, everybody – it's party time!

Cheers from all but BENNY *and* TRACY, *who look glum.*

PAULA: Oh good!

CRAIG: I love games!

BENNY (*to* TRACY): Sickening, isn't it? All this enforced cheerfulness – puts me off my food.

TRACY: You mean *my* food – *you* didn't bring any!

BENNY: Details, details.

MR COOPER: Before Paula and Craig show us their display of knot-tying –

AVRIL: Sir!

MR COOPER: Yes, Avril?

AVRIL: I thought they were supposed to be showing us their knots.

MR COOPER: They will be.

AVRIL: But you just said they were *not* tying!

Groans.

MR COOPER: Very good, Avril. However, before we are treated to that I thought we could get to know each other a little better.

TRACY: But we all know each other already, Sir – we're all from the same class at school.

MRS COOPER: What Mr Cooper means, Tracy, is that we'll talk about ourselves and share our views with each other.

JULIAN: Like on the telly, Miss? Like on the talk shows?

MR COOPER: A bit like that, Julian.

AVRIL: That's right up your street, Julian. You love talking about yourself.

JULIAN: No more than you do, Avril!

AVRIL: True . . .

MR COOPER: Well, let's talk about what we'll do when we all leave school.

JUDY: What about you, Sir?

MR COOPER: I'm not likely to leave school – I'm a teacher! What about you, Judy? What would you like to do?

JUDY: Well . . . I'd like to be a vet – an animal doctor.

JULIAN: But you're afraid of animals, Judy!

JUDY: Not the cute little ones like kittens and puppies with fluffy fur and tiny little noses!

JULIAN: ⎱
AVRIL ⎰ Aw!

JUDY: I love little baby animals.

MRS COOPER: What about the rest of you? How about you, Paula? What would you like to do?

PAULA: I'd like to be a policewoman or maybe join the Wrens, Miss!

CRAIG: And I want to be a soldier!

PAULA: Me and Craig love working in a team. That right, Craig?

CRAIG: You bet!

BENNY (*aside, gazing up to heaven*): Dad! What have you made me do? I can't stand it!

MR COOPER: What about you, Benny? Have you any ambitions for the future?

BENNY: Yessir, I want to go home tomorrow.

Laughter.

MR COOPER: Come on, Benny – surely you have some idea?

BENNY: Well . . .

ALL: Go on!

BENNY: If you want to know, I want to be a magician – a hypnotist.

Laughter.

MRS COOPER: That's interesting, Benny. Tell us more.

BENNY: Well, Miss, I reckon a hypnotist is better than an ordinary magician because he has power over people – not just cards and rabbits.

MRS COOPER: I see.

BENNY: Yeah, and I like the idea of being the star, just like a pop star, only better 'cos I'm in control of my audience.

MR COOPER: Benny, have you ever tried to hypnotise anyone before?

ROYSTON: Please, Sir, he's tried it on me before.

BENNY: That's right, Sir. I told him to act like an idiot, but nothing happened.

MR COOPER: So there was no change?

BENNY: Hard to say, Sir: Royston's always been an idiot.

Laughter.

AVRIL: Do some more, Benny!

JULIAN: Get out your book – the one on hypnosis.
BENNY: Shall I?
ALL: Yes!
BENNY: All right then – I'll get it!

　　Exit BENNY.

TRACY: Hey, Sir! Let's go along with him, just for fun.
　　We know he can't hypnotise anybody, but he really
　　thinks he's a walking wonder! Can we, Sir, Miss?
MR COOPER: Okay – just this once, just for fun. (*Aside, to*
　　MRS COOPER) It won't do his ego any harm to be
　　deflated a little.
ALL: Great! Whoopee! (*etc.*)

　　Enter BENNY *with book*.

BENNY: Here we are. (*Reads*) *Hypnotism Made Easy* by
　　Amina Trantz.

　　Laughter.

BENNY: All right – who's first then?
AVRIL: I'll go first!
BENNY: Right. Stand up.

　　AVRIL *stands up*.

BENNY: Look into my eyes . . . You are getting sleepy
　　. . . (*looks into his book*) Let's see now – ah yes. (*Looks up.*)
　　Very slee-eepy.

　　AVRIL *closes her eyes*.

AVRIL: I . . . am . . . very . . . slee-eepy.
BENNY: You hear only my voice.
AVRIL: I . . . hear . . . only . . . your . . . voice.
BENNY: Obey only my commands!
AVRIL: I . . . obey . . . only . . . your . . . commands.

During this time, ROYSTON *really has been mesmerised and goes into a trance. Nobody notices.*

BENNY: Listen to my command. After the count of three you will be a chicken. You will wake up and be normal again only when I say the word 'sausages'! Do you understand me?

AVRIL:
ROYSTON: } Yes, Master.

BENNY: One, two, three!

AVRIL *and* ROYSTON *make loud chicken noises and strut around the camp.* ROYSTON *struts off into the forest — everybody thinks he is joking except* BENNY. *Everybody laughs.*

BENNY: Sausages!

AVRIL (*pretending to wake up*): Well, are you going to start then?

BENNY: Start? I've finished! It's over!

AVRIL: So much for your claims, Mr Master Hypnotist. Hm-m, I'm feeling a bit *peckish*. I'm always in a *fowl* mood when I'm hungry.

JUDY: You've been ever so brave, Avril.

JULIAN: Yeah, that took some *pluck*, that did.

JUDY: *Eggs*actly!

Laughter.

BENNY: You mean you don't remember anything?

AVRIL: Nah. You haven't done anything yet!

BENNY: All right — who's next? Just so I can prove to Avril here I'm not a fake. How about you, Paula?

PAULA: I'm game!

JULIAN (*pointing to* AVRIL): So was she!

Laughter.

BENNY: Here we go!

BENNY repeats the process of hypnosis with at least one reference to the book. This is a good opportunity for the actors to improvise.

BENNY: At the count of three you will be a dog – a German Shepherd! You will return to normal when I clap my hands. Understand?

PAULA: Yes, Master.

BENNY: One, two, three!

PAULA acts like a dog – the actor can improvise – and chases CRAIG around the stage.

CRAIG: Down, girl!

BENNY: Paula, sit!

PAULA sits next to BENNY.

BENNY: You are still a dog, but you are a talking dog. How do you feel now?

PAULA (*in a barking voice*): Rough!

Laughter.

AVRIL: What does tree-bark feel like, Paula?

PAULA: Rough!

More laughter.

JULIAN: What does sandpaper feel like, Paula?

PAULA: Rough . . . but only if you scrape your finger against it!

More laughter, and now BENNY realises the joke they have been playing against him. He is annoyed.

BENNY: Oh, very funny!

PAULA: We're only having a little joke, Benny – don't take it to heart.

BENNY: You don't believe me, do you? (*Looks around*)
    None of you do! But I *can* hypnotise – I *can*! But you've
    got to co-operate. How can I do it if you don't even *try*?
MR COOPER: Will you give me a chance, Benny?
BENNY: Honest, Sir? Will you do it properly?
MR COOPER: I'll do everything you tell me to do, Benny.
BENNY: Great! Right then (*looks in his book*) I'm taking no
    chances this time. (*Pulls out a watch on a chain.*) This is my
    dad's best watch – he, er, let me borrow it for a while.
    Now look very carefully . . .

*Here the hypnosis can be improvised using the watch twisting
on its chain.*

BENNY: Aha! Mr Cooper, are you paying attention?
MR COOPER: Yes, Master!

Laughter.

BENNY: When I count to three you will be a ferocious
    gorilla until I say the word 'bananas', then you will be
    your normal self.
TRACY: That is his normal self, isn't it?
MRS COOPER: Be careful, Tracy.
TRACY: Sorry, Miss!
BENNY: Do you understand, Mr Cooper?
MR COOPER (*keeping up the act*): I understand, Master.
BENNY: One, two, three!

    MR COOPER *starts to scratch his armpits, then jumps up
    and down, making appropriate noises. Much laughter from the*
    CHILDREN.

BENNY: I did it!
TRACY: Hey, Mrs Cooper! What do monkeys do their
    toast on?
MRS COOPER: I don't know, Tracy: what do monkeys do
    their toast on?

TRACY: G'rillas!

Laughter. MR COOPER *then makes more loud gorilla noises and runs into the forest. A loud cock-crow is then heard off stage.*

AVRIL: What was that? Roosters don't crow at night!

CRAIG: Where's Royston?

JUDY: He's not here – oh no! He must really have been hypnotised, and he thinks he's a chicken.

BENNY: Ah, to have so much power, and still only in the second year!

MRS COOPER: This is no joke, Benny; if Royston really is hypnotised he might hurt himself. We'll have to get him back here at once!

BENNY: Yes, sorry, Miss. And we'll have to get Mr Cooper too. Shall we –

Enter NOSHER, *brandishing a pistol, followed by* SID, *holding a small branch in a threatening way. There are screams of alarm from the* CHILDREN.

NOSHER: What nice, cosy party have we here, then?

SID: Ooh, goody! I like parties, Nosher!

NOSHER: That's good, Sid, 'cos we're going to have a lovely little party with these nice people.

With his gun he motions all the CHILDREN *to one side of the stage, with* MRS COOPER *standing protectively in front of them.*

MRS COOPER: Who are you, and what do you want?

NOSHER: Don't get excited, lady – we won't harm you: not if you do as you're told.

SID: No, lady – I won't harm you – I like parties!

NOSHER: My little friend is right – we both like parties. (*Points the gun at* MRS COOPER.) Now, lady – get us some food, and be quick about it!

MRS COOPER: You mustn't harm the children, whatever else you do!

SID: I like kids, Miss.

NOSHER: Shut up, Sid! We're not here to run a kids' party!

SID: No, Nosher?

NOSHER: No!

SID (*disappointed*): Oh!

    BENNY *steps up to* NOSHER, *waving his father's watch on its chain.*

TRACY: Benny! Don't be a fool!

MRS COOPER: No, Benny!

BENNY: Don't worry, Miss – I know what I'm doing! (*Stares at* NOSHER) You are getting sleepy . . . very slee-eepy.

    SID *starts nodding off.*

NOSHER (*taking the watch*): Thanks, kid – I always fancied a fancy watch!

BENNY (*shocked*): But . . . I thought . . .

NOSHER (*threateningly*): Thought what, kid? I'll do all the thinking here! (*Sees* SID *in a trance and shoves him.*) Hey, you!

SID: Wha . . . Who . . . Me? Oh, I was having a nice sleep, Nosher!

NOSHER: You're always half-asleep, stupid!

    SID *looks hurt.*

NOSHER (*pointing gun threateningly*): Lady – we want food – now!

MRS COOPER: Avril, get some food from the packs for these people.

    AVRIL *goes to the packs and starts rummaging.* MRS COOPER *turns to* NOSHER.

MRS COOPER: Then you'll go?

NOSHER: Not just yet – we'll stick around for a while! You two (*looks at* CRAIG *and* PAULA), you've got some rope?

CRAIG: ⎱
PAULA: ⎰ Yessir!

> CRAIG *and* PAULA *go to their packs and get rope.*

NOSHER: Okay kids – tie everybody's hands. Sid, when they've finished, you can tie them up.

SID: Right, Nosh.

> PAULA *and* CRAIG *begin tying* JUDY, JULIAN, TRACY, MRS COOPER *and* BENNY.

TRACY: I suppose you think you're brave, robbing defenceless children!

> TRACY *kicks* SID *on the shin.* SID *hops in pain.*

SID: Ow! Don't kick me, girlie! Nosher's the brave one – I ain't brave at all!

NOSHER (*angrily pointing gun at* TRACY): Don't try that again, you little monkey, or you won't be able to kick anything ever again! And you hurry up with those ropes! And just to make sure nobody else has any stupid fool ideas about kicking and punching, you can tie up everybody's feet as well! Sit down, the lot of you!

> EVERYBODY *hurriedly sits down, including* SID.

NOSHER: Not you, Sid, you little twerp! Who do you think this lot are – your pals?

SID (*getting up quickly and looking embarrassed*): No, Nosh, 'course not, wouldn't dream of it . . .

> CRAIG *and* PAULA *have begun the task of tying up everybody's feet.* TRACY *is making it difficult for them.*

MRS COOPER: Oh, Tracy, don't provoke them again!

BENNY: Mrs Cooper's right, Tracy – they're dangerous!

NOSHER: The boy's right there. You just do as you're told.

AVRIL *comes over with various different packages of food.*

NOSHER: Ah, good! Food! (*turning to* CRAIG *and* PAULA) Hey, you two, come and tie up your little lady friend here! Sid, tie up those two when they've finished.

CRAIG *ties* AVRIL, *while* SID *ties* PAULA. *Finally* SID *ties* CRAIG.

NOSHER: Good, very good. Now then, Sid – let's eat!

SID *and* NOSHER *tuck into the food while the bound-up group of* CHILDREN *glower at them angrily. Suddenly they all jump in fright as a weird, ape-like scream echoes out of the forest off-stage.*

SID: W-what w-was that, Nosher?

NOSHER (*trying not to be afraid*): Just some stupid animal – eat your food.

JUDY: It's a monster!

BENNY (*to* TRACY, *in a stage whisper*): It must be Mr Cooper! He's still out there, and he thinks he's a gorilla!

SID: At least there weren't no animals in prison, Nosher!

TRACY: I can see at least two that escaped.

MRS COOPER: So you are escaped prisoners! Just as I thought!

NOSHER (*sarcastically*): There's no hiding anything from you, lady, is there? (*Looks around*) Are you the only grown-up here, then? . . . Well? Speak up!

JUDY: No – Mr Cooper –

MRS COOPER (*cutting* JUDY *short*): Mr Cooper, my husband, will be back tomorrow morning with some more supplies.

NOSHER: Hmm. Well, we can all stop worrying, then, eh? We're supposed to be having a party, aren't we? Relax!

All sit. NOSHER *and* SID *carry on eating.*

NOSHER (*looking at* PAULA): Hey, you! You can collect all the money your friends have got while they entertain us. Sid, untie her.
SID: Right, Nosh.

SID *unties* PAULA. PAULA *slowly examines bags and pockets and collects any money she finds. She whispers to each of them as she does so, making furtive gestures at their bonds. Meanwhile* NOSHER *has started speaking again.*

NOSHER: Now, I suppose you were going to tell each other tales around the camp fire or something like that, eh? So why don't we do just that? You! (*Looks at* JUDY) You can start.
MRS COOPER: Leave the girl alone – can't you see she's frightened?
JUDY: It's . . . it's all right, Miss. Er . . . well . . . oh, yes, when I was a little girl my mother used to tell me a story about a little lost kitten called Tiddles . . .
AVRIL:
JULIAN: } Aw!
NOSHER: That's enough – I don't want to hear about little lost kittens!
SID: Aw, Nosher – don't you like little kittens? They're all fluffy and cute and –
NOSHER: Sid! Grow up! (SID *looks offended.*) Now – who's got a proper story? No kid's stuff this time!
BENNY: I know a story – a true story.
SID: Oh, good! Let's hear it.
NOSHER: Go on, kid.
BENNY: It's about the Woodwose.

NOSHER: Woodwose? Never heard of it! What's a woodwose, anyway? Sounds like a termite!

BENNY: It's not a termite – it's much bigger than that. You've heard of the Yeti in Tibet and the Sasquatch or Bigfoot in Canada? Huge ape-like creatures that live in the wild?

SID: L–like the Abomina–b–ble Snowman, you mean?

BENNY: That's right.

SID: Ooh, I don't like the sound of that, Nosher.

NOSHER: Shut up, Sid. Go on, you.

BENNY: This very forest is said to be inhabited by Trolls – ogres of the forest which the old Anglo-Saxons over a thousand years ago called the Woodwose – the guardians of the forest against evil.

JUDY: I told you there was a monster! We read about them in school!

A cock-crow is heard off-stage.

NOSHER: That's your monster, you stupid kid! A chicken!

SID: At night, Nosher?

BENNY: He does no harm, this Woodwose, this spirit-ape, until his domain is disturbed – and then . . . (*he shudders expressively.*)

An inhuman, ape-like scream is heard off-stage. JUDY screams.

SID: Ow! Nosher! Help!

NOSHER: Be quiet, Sid, it's only a story. (*Tries to put on a show of bravado.*) I ain't afraid! Go on, kid.

BENNY: There have been several mysterious deaths over the years in this forest – bodies found among the trees . . . and nobody really knows *how* they died.

MRS COOPER: What the boy says is true. I remember reading accounts myself in the newspapers about such deaths . . . about a year ago for the last one.

BENNY: Yes, Miss. Some were found with a look of horror on their faces . . . as if they had died of fright!

Right on cue, another ape-like scream is heard off-stage.

SID (*really frightened*): Nosher! I'm afraid . . . there's a monster out there!

NOSHER (*also afraid but trying to hide it*): There's something – but it ain't no monster.

SID: I'm telling you – it's the abomim-bably – the abomimabooble – it's the ape-man!

NOSHER: All right, Sid! If you're so sure this kid's woodlouse is out there –

BENNY: It's called a wood*wose*.

NOSHER: Whatever! Anyway, Sid, I think you should go and have a look to make certain.

SID: Wha . . . ! Me? I can't – I hate monsters!

NOSHER (*angrily*): Sid! Take one of this lot with you to keep you company. (*He drags* CRAIG *out from the group.*) Here, you can go with him!

SID: Why can't you go, Nosher?

TRACY: 'Cos he's afraid!

NOSHER (*busy untying* CRAIG): Shut up, kid – I ain't afraid of nothing, but I'm in charge here and I'm the one who looks after you lot! Now go on, Sid!

SID: Aw, Nosher – do I have to?

NOSHER: Yes!

SID (*to* CRAIG): Come on then, fella – you first! What's your name?

CRAIG: Craig.

SID: Mine's Sid. Pleased to meet you.

They shake hands. NOSHER *thumps the ground in impatience.*

NOSHER: Sid! This ain't a prayer-meeting! Get on with it!

SID: Yes, Nosh.

They shuffle out, SID holding his only weapon – a small branch.

TRACY (*to* NOSHER): You're a coward!

Silence for about five seconds. An ape-like scream is heard, then two human screams – one obviously SID's – then silence. JUDY starts to cry.

TRACY: Now see what you've done – you murderer!
NOSHER: I didn't do anything! Anyway, Sid was getting to be a drag, a nuisance. I'm better off without him.
BENNY: And what about Craig?
AVRIL: Don't you care what's happened to him?
JUDY: You brute!
MRS COOPER: When will you stop? Aren't two lives enough for you? Why don't you give yourself up?
NOSHER: Be quiet, lady – I didn't kill them! They were asking for it – it was – it was –

Ape-like scream is heard again, very close this time.

NOSHER (*cries in alarm*): It was that – that thing that did it! (*Waves his gun around.*)

JUDY: The Woodwose! The Woodwose! He's coming!

NOSHER: No! (*Fires three shots into the forest*) Take that, whatever you are!

More screams, from the 'woodwose' and the girls on stage. NOSHER cries out.

MRS COOPER: Give yourself up, Nosher!
NOSHER: One more word out of you and you're next! (*Points gun threateningly.*)
BENNY: Coward!
TRACY: Killer!

More ape-screams.

NOSHER: Shut up! Shut up! (*Fires two shots into the bush*) The next one's for you, teacher! Keep still!

MR COOPER *rushes in, screaming like an ape, followed by* CRAIG. NOSHER *screams, temporarily frozen with shock; meanwhile all the children are shedding their bonds, only slip-knotted by* CRAIG *and* PAULA, *and as soon as he is up* BENNY *knocks the gun out of* NOSHER'S *hands.* CRAIG *immediately throws a rope around him. He begins to struggle, but* TRACY *crouches behind him and* MRS COOPER *pushes him so that he trips and falls over* TRACY. *Before he can get up again* CRAIG *has finished off his bonds.* NOSHER *is lying in a tied-up heap, helpless as a well-trussed chicken!*

ALL: Hooray!

JUDY: Mr Cooper! Sir! Were you really the ape-man?

MR COOPER: Yes! I was just going to go along with Benny's hypnotism for fun, but when I saw the two convicts arrive I stayed hidden in the trees. I thought I might be able to surprise them somehow.

NOSHER: So it was only a teacher! Caught out by a rotten teacher!

MR COOPER: Oh no – it was the children who caught you out, Nosher. Benny knew Sid was already nervous, so he started telling wild-man stories to frighten you both. With a little help from me!

MRS COOPER: But thank God, you're safe now – oh, Arthur! (*She hugs him.*)

MR COOPER: Celia! (*Kisses her.*)

AVRIL: ⎱ Aw!
JULIAN: ⎰

NOSHER: So where's Sid, the little twerp?

CRAIG (*proudly*): He's tied up in the forest – and the knots on his rope are real ones, too! Not like the slip-knots me and Paula used for the rest of you!

BENNY (*slapping* CRAIG *and* PAULA *on the back*): Yeah, those trick knots were great! It hardly took any time for me to free my hands and go for Nosher's gun!

PAULA (*proud but bashful*): Good teamwork, Benny.

BENNY:
CRAIG: } You bet!

MR COOPER (*looking at* NOSHER, *who is still futilely struggling*): I can't speak for Nosher here, but I think Sid is only too glad to be getting back to the safety of prison after the fright he had. When he saw me he fainted!

Laughter.

CRAIG: I nearly did too an' all sir! You weren't half convincing.

More laughter. Enter two POLICEMEN, *with* SID *in handcuffs. One policeman carries a gun.*

POLICEMAN 1: Everybody stand still! This is the police!

They notice NOSHER.

POLICEMAN 2: Oh! You all seem to have everything in hand already! Well done!

NOSHER: See what you've done, Sid?

SID: Aw, shut up, Nosher! I'd rather be back in prison – at least it's safe there!

POLICEMAN 1: We'll take care of these two now. They escaped from prison three days ago.

POLICEMAN 2: Yes, and that one (*indicates* NOSHER) knocked me out and stole my gun!

BENNY (*proudly holding out the gun, but in a nonchalant voice*): This the one, officer?

POLICEMAN 2: Thank you, young man! (*Takes the gun*) That was very brave of you – it was very brave of you all!

NOSHER (*to himself*): I should have hit him harder!

POLICEMAN 1: A fine example of teamwork!

POLICEMAN 2: Well, we'll take care of these two now. Do you need any help?

MR COOPER: No thank you, officer – I think we can manage now.

MRS COOPER: But what about Royston? Where is he?

BENNY: Yeah – I forgot all about him! Did I really hypnotise him?

MR COOPER: Yes, you did!

BENNY: But . . . not you, Sir?

MR COOPER: Sorry, Benny – no! But we must find Royston before he lands himself in some kind of trouble!

A cock-crow is heard off-stage.

TRACY: That's him! He thinks he's a chicken!

All call out ROYSTON's name. Enter ROYSTON strutting and clucking.

MR COOPER: Royston! Wake up! Can't you hear me? (*Turns to BENNY*) Benny! What was that word you chose to get him out of this?

BENNY: Er . . . (*Pause. BENNY looks stricken.*) I can't remember! Oh, I wish I'd never heard of hypnotism now!

TRACY: It was some kind of food, wasn't it? Er . . . turkey?

AVRIL: Noodles?

JULIAN: Hamburgers?

MRS COOPER: We can't have him spending the rest of his life as a chicken, Benny!

TRACY: Why not? He's managed for thirteen years so far!

Laughter.

MR COOPER: Be serious – come on, Benny! What was it?

BENNY (*smiling with relief*): I've got it!

ALL: Yes?

BENNY (*facing ROYSTON*): Omelettes!

ROYSTON: Cluck.

ALL: Uh!

BENNY: No, no – ah, now I've got it for certain! (*Faces* ROYSTON) Sausages!

ROYSTON (*stops chicken act*): What are you all staring at me for? (*Sees* CONVICTS *and* POLICEMEN) Who're they?

ALL: Hooray!
    Good old Royston!
    Welcome back!
    Etc., etc.

MRS COOPER: Thank goodness!

POLICEMAN 1: Well, now that's sorted out, we really will be on our way with the prisoners.

POLICEMAN 2: Yes, and thanks again. We'll be in touch. Well done, everybody! Goodbye!

   Exit with CONVICTS, SID *saying goodbye quite happily.*

MR COOPER: Well, Benny, do you still want to be a hypnotist? You know you can really do it now – sometimes!

BENNY: Nah, Sir, I want to be a policeman.

TRACY (*astonished*): A policeman? You?

BENNY: Yeah – if it hadn't been for our great teamwork we might never have got out of that fix. When I saw the police arrive I finally knew what I wanted to be – part of a team.

TRACY: You're right, Benny. Wow, perhaps even our parents were right an' all! Perhaps we have been thinking too much of ourselves.

MRS COOPER: That's great, you two! So you want to be part of the team from now on?

BENNY: ⎫
TRACY: ⎬ Yes!

MRS COOPER: Good! Since those convicts ate our dinner, how about making a start by getting the supper?

Laughter from the OTHER CHILDREN.

BENNY: ⎫
TRACY: ⎬ Aw, Miss!

ROYSTON: Good idea, Miss! I'm starving! What're we having?

MRS COOPER: Chicken sandwiches!

All except ROYSTON *laugh and make chicken sounds.*

ROYSTON (*facing the audience, with his hands spread in a gesture of complete bewilderment*): So what did I say that's so funny?

[*Curtain*]

Playing for Time
or
What Professor What Did About the Which

(With apologies to the producers of *Dr Who*, *Star Trek*, *Star Wars*, etc.)

CHARACTERS

SANDY, *a schoolgirl (or boy)*
SANDY'S MOTHER *(or father)*

Cadets
CAPTAIN SPIKE
STELLA
CORNELIA
GROUNDLINGS 1 *to* 10 (*no.* 10 *a.k.a.* CYRIL)

Time Lords
PROFESSOR WHAT
TYRANTULA *the Time Which* (*a.k.a.* MISS WHICH)
ASTRA/AMANDA (*two parts, same actress*)

Pirates
REG THE RAVAGER
HORACE
BORIS
DORIS (*a reporter*)

In Germany:
LUDWIG VAN BEETHOVEN
HANS, *the butler*

In Greece
KING ODYSSEUS
QUEEN PENELOPE
THESAURUS, *the Pun-Dragon*
SOLDIERS 1 *and* 2, *and various others*
GIRLS 1 *and* 2
VARIOUS SPECTATORS

SCENE 1: Sandy's house
SCENE 2: A lonely street at night
SCENE 3: Inside the M.A.S.T.E.R.
SCENE 4: A forest in Germany
SCENE 5: A wood with a temple in Ancient Greece
SCENE 6: A lonely street at night (same as for Scene 2)

Properties
Sandy's book
Rubbish skip
Three dustbins
Rayguns, cutlasses, spears; various other weapons and
    armour for the pirates, Ancient Greeks and Groundlings.
Black box plus aerial to represent transmitter
Large lever for the sleep-ray
Photographic equipment and reporter's notebook for Doris
Glitter-dust to represent Circe's magic powder
Feather to represent quill for Beethoven
Music manuscript-paper for Beethoven
Cigarette-holder for the Pun-Dragon

Scene 1

Sandy's House. Enter SANDY *and her* MOTHER. MOTHER
is carrying a book.

SANDY: Are you *sure* the repair-man can't make it, Mum?

MOTHER: I'm sorry, Sandy, but the video set's broken
down and that's that. The repair-man can't come to fix it
till tomorrow.

SANDY: Aw, Mum! This is so boring! Stuck inside on a
wet Saturday afternoon with nothing to do – no video to
watch and only party political broadcasts on the telly! I'll
die of boredom!

MOTHER: Well, you could always try reading a good
book.

SANDY: Reading? Only nerds read.

MOTHER: Come on, you can survive for once without
watching a video, you know. Give it a try.

SANDY: You *know* I hate reading, Mum!

MOTHER (*waving the book in front of her*): Oh, go on, try
this book that your Auntie Angela bought you for your
birthday. You haven't even looked at it yet.

SANDY: Aw, Mum!

MOTHER: Go on, it'll keep you out of the way for a while
– do you good. (*Hands* SANDY *the book.*)

SANDY (*grudgingly*): Oh, all right.

    Exit MOTHER.

SANDY (*to audience*): She's always on about reading – says I
don't read enough. (*Glances briefly at book*) I *hate* reading!
(*Glances again*) What's this then? (*Reads title of the book*)
'Playing for Time, or What Professor What Did About
the Which – a Choose-Your-Own-Adventure Story'. (*To
audience again*) Huh! I'd rather watch 'Teenage Ninja
Aardvarks v. the Mutant Killer Tomatoes' on the video.
That's what I like – just to sit back and be entertained.

Not like reading, that's too much like school! (*Sighs*) Oh, well. I suppose I'll give it a try, there's nothing else to do . . . You want to hear some? Go on, keep me company. (*Reads aloud from the book*) 'Instructions to the reader: Be alert! Just when you least expect it, you the reader have to make choices and decide just where this exciting science-fiction fantasy will lead. Read on . . .' Sounds weird! Well, here goes.

SANDY *moves stage left, sits in a chair facing the audience where she reads the book.* SANDY *remains on stage in dimmed lighting during the action but is spotlit when she speaks. The background set is now highlighted ready for scene two.*

Scene 2

A lonely street at night. At the back of the stage to one side is a large rubbish-skip. Three dustbins are on the other side. Enter the GROUNDLINGS *in a rush shouting excitedly. There are about ten of them and they are of mixed races from different planets, so they can look however you like. They are dressed in futuristic costumes of a military but punkish nature and are in a very angry mood. They stop in centre stage.*

GROUNDLING 1: I saw them here a moment ago.

GROUNDLING 2: Where are they then?

GROUNDLING 3: I wanted to bash 'em!

GROUNDLING 4: Tar and feather 'em!

GROUNDLING 5: Skin 'em alive!

GROUNDLING 6: Mash 'em!

GROUNDLING 7: Smash 'em!

GROUNDLING 8: Mangle 'em!

GROUNDLING 9: Strangle 'em!

GROUNDLING 10 (CYRIL) (*lisping*): Be extremely unpleasant towards them. (*The others look at him*) Well, can't I play then?

GROUNDLING 1: Enough of that! Let's split up – five of
  us go this way (*he points stage right*), the rest of us go this
  way (*pointing stage left*). Meet back here in five minutes.
  Right?

GROUNDLINGS: Right!

GROUNDLING 1: Then let's get 'em!

They all rush off as GROUNDLING 1 *directed, shouting
dire threats of Bash 'em, Smash 'em, etc. Once they have gone
the lids slowly lift from the three dustbins. We see the heads of*
SPIKE, CORNELIA *and* STELLA. CORNELIA *has
pointed ears.*

CORNELIA: Whew! That was close!

STELLA: Have they gone, Spike?

SPIKE: I think so, Stella, but you can bet they'll be back
  soon – you heard them!

CORNELIA: And my super-sensitive Omegan ears can
  hear them even now.

SPIKE: What are they saying, Cornelia?

CORNELIA: Well, there's good news and bad news . . .

STELLA: What's the good news?

CORNELIA: They want to take us to dinner.

STELLA: Oh good!

SPIKE: What's the bad news?

CORNELIA: We *are* the dinner!

Groans from the others.

SPIKE: Come on, we can't stay here. Let's get out and
  make a plan.

STELLA: You're the captain.

*They get out from the dustbins. They are in futuristic cadet
gear.*

STELLA: So what's your plan, Captain Spike?

CORNELIA: And make it snappy, they've started to turn back – I can hear them.

SPIKE: Let's see. (*Pause*) I'm afraid we'll have to fight for it.

A voice is heard off-stage.

VOICE (ASTRA's): There will be no need for that, Captain Spike.

SPIKE: Who said that?

CORNELIA (*pointing to the skip*): It came from over there.

ASTRA steps out from behind the skip – a beautiful young woman in futuristic dress.

ASTRA: Don't be afraid. I'm here to help you.

SPIKE: Who are you?

ASTRA: There's no time for explanations. (*Pointing to the skip*) Step this way before your pursuers return.

STELLA: They'd find us there in no time! We'll have to fight, Spike!

CORNELIA: They're nearly here! What shall we do, Captain?

Sounds of returning GROUNDLINGS are heard. Lights dim and all on stage 'freeze' in position. Spotlight on SANDY)

SANDY: Well, what are you waiting for?

All the 'frozen' characters turn their heads and glare at her.

SANDY: What, me? Why? Oh, I get it! (*looks down at the book again*) Now, let's have a look . . . There's three choices.
   a) Follow the girl;
   b) Fight and get mashed, bashed and smashed etc.;
   c) Do nothing and still get mashed, bashed and smashed etc.
I don't call that much of a choice! I think we'd better

follow the girl, don't you? Now then, 'choice a), turn to page ten' . . .

Lights dim on SANDY, *who goes on reading, and come back up on the main stage.* CHARACTERS *'unfreeze'.*

SPIKE: We've nothing to lose – come on, you two! Okay, Miss, lead the way.

They follow ASTRA, *who takes them to a door at the side of the skip.*

STELLA: I never noticed that door before!
CORNELIA: What's a door doing in the side of a rubbish skip?
STELLA: I give up. What *is* a door doing in the side of a rubbish skip?
SPIKE: Hey! Get in quickly, or *we*'ll be rubbished by those Groundlings!
STELLA: I'd rather be trashed than bashed – let's go!

They follow ASTRA *inside. Lights down.*

Scene 3

Inside the M.A.S.T.E.R.. It is the interior of a spaceship with lots of lights, levers and dials. There is one large lever to the rear of centre stage. Enter ASTRA *with* SPIKE, CORNELIA, *and* STELLA *following close behind and gazing round in amazement.*

STELLA: Impossible! This place is bigger on the inside than it is on the outside!
CORNELIA: This would appear to be a clear case of the theory of inter-dimensional exchange being demonstrated in practice.
STELLA: It would?

Enter PROFESSOR WHAT *dressed in the clothes of a late-nineteenth-century gentleman, wearing a smoking-jacket and cap.*

PROFESSOR: It would indeed! An excellent piece of deduction, young lady. Now, would you, Sir, care to join me for cigars and brandy while the ladies retire to the drawing-room?

ASTRA: Professor! You've got your time-zones mixed up again! This is 2192, not 1892 – and how dare you leave us ladies out of it!

STELLA (*indignantly*): Yes, how dare you!

SPIKE: Hang on a minute! Now before we go any further – just *who* are *you*, and *where* are *we*? And what's all this about 'time-zones'?

PROFESSOR: No, old chap, I'm not Who – he's my cousin.

CORNELIA: What?

PROFESSOR: That's right.

SPIKE: What's right?

PROFESSOR: Well, modesty forbids me to say I'm right *all* of the time, but I think I'm pretty clued up –

STELLA: But *who* are you?

PROFESSOR: Not Who, my dear. I'm What . . . oh dear, I thought I'd told you that already!

ASTRA: I think I'd better explain.

SPIKE: I think you'd better!

ASTRA (*indicating the* PROFESSOR): This is Professor What.

CORNELIA: Who?

STELLA: Oh no! Let's not go through all *that* again! She means his *name* is 'What' – right, Miss Whoever-you-are?

PROFESSOR (*indicating* ASTRA): This is my assistant, Astra; and I am Professor What.

SPIKE: Pleased to meet you, I'm sure.

PROFESSOR: Delighted to make your acquaintance, Mr
    Sure.

SPIKE: No, Professor, my name is Spike – Captain Spike.

PROFESSOR: I wish you'd make your mind up, old chap!
    Still, I'm pleased to meet you, Captain Spike, and all of
    you.

ASTRA: Professor, we've done the best we can with the
    repairs. Shouldn't we try moving on . . .?

PROFESSOR: What? . . . oh yes, Astra. Yes, let's give the
    ship a test run across a couple of centuries.

SPIKE: But hold on, Professor, we still don't know where
    we are or why we are here!

CORNELIA: Intriguing!

STELLA: Creepy, I call it.

ASTRA: There will be time for explanations later.
    Professor! The Master Switch!

PROFESSOR: Of course, my dear.

> *He twiddles with a control panel and pulls a lever on it.
> There is a flashing of stroboscopic lights, a 'cosmic' sound, and
> they all move as if they are being tossed about in slow motion.
> This lasts for about ten seconds, then they stop and normal
> lighting is resumed.*

STELLA: What was *that*?

PROFESSOR: Oh my cosmic aunt! That was a most
    unusual inter-dimensional time bump.

> *Enter* REG THE RAVAGER *with* BORIS *and*
> HORACE. REG *is dressed like a cross between Darth Vader
> and Long John Silver.* BORIS *and* HORACE *are dressed in
> suitable space-pirate gear and are bristling with ray-guns and
> cutlasses.*

REG: That weren't no time-bump, you lubbers! That were
    me! Reg the Ravager, space-pirate and scourge of the
    Galaxy –

BORIS: and Mars —
HORACE: and the Milky Way —
BORIS: }
HORACE: } Yum yum! Lovely choccies! etc.
REG: Avast behind there!
BORIS: Who has?
HORACE: Can't be me, matey, I've been on a diet!
BORIS (*chuckling*): Perhaps he means himself.
REG (*sharply*): Boris!
BORIS (*jumping to attention*): Here, Cap'n!
REG: Horace!
HORACE: Here, Cap'n!
REG: Doris! (*Pause; no response*) Doris!

DORIS *enters in a rush. She is dressed as a journalist and carries lots of camera equipment, a tape-recorder, notebook and pencil. Her camera must have an automatic flash.*

DORIS: Sorry I'm late, Captain, I was just loading my camera and tape-recorder.
REG: Come on, Doris, you're slowing me up!
PROFESSOR: What is the meaning of this intrusion?
DORIS: Allow me to introduce myself! Doris McStarr, ace reporter for the 'Space Pirates' Monthly Gazette'. I'm doing a feature on Mr Ravager for next month's issue.
HORACE: Ar!
BORIS: That she be!
DORIS: Now then, ladies and gentlemen, let's have a nice pose for the camera, Pirates with Victims.

All group in a pose for the camera.

DORIS: Smile please!

All give cheesy grins as DORIS takes a few pictures. Improvise DORIS adjusting their poses to suit her idea of a good shot.

DORIS: Lovely! That'll do for now, thank you.

All resume their former positions, PIRATES *holding the* CREW *at bay with ray-guns.*

REG: Back to business, lads!

HORACE: ⎫
BORIS: ⎬ Ar, Cap'n!

STELLA: Who are these idiots?

SPIKE: Quiet, Stella, let's not make any sudden moves — those guns are real.

REG: We saw your funny little space-bucket appear in our territory, and grabbed you in our tractor-beam. We've beamed aboard to rob you of all your treasure, and you can't move until we done it!

ASTRA: Treasure? What treasure? We haven't any treasure!

PROFESSOR: That's right. Absolutely no hidden treasure whatever.

ASTRA: Professor . . .?

REG: *Hidden* treasure, eh?

BORIS: Can I zap 'em, Cap'n? Can I? Can I?

HORACE: No, it's my turn! You did all the zappin' last time, when you zapped all the teachers at your galactic school reunion!

BORIS: So did you!

HORACE: Didn't!

BORIS: Did!

HORACE: Didn't!

BORIS: Did!

REG: Pipe down, you snivellin' little space-fleas! I'm the cap'n an' I give the orders! Doris'll do the zappin'!

BORIS: ⎫
HORACE: ⎬ Aw!

REG: Ar! That's right, Doris, now you can find out what it's really like to be a nasty mean space pirate!

DORIS (*impressed*): Ooh, Captain!

REG (*handing over a ray-gun*): I've set it on stun so's it won't put us off our tea.

DORIS: Ooh, thanks. (*She takes out her microphone and recorder and faces the audience, putting on a typical news reporter's voice.*) And so here we are in the middle of a tense situation deep in the heart of the Gamma Six system. Let us see how the desperate victims of this cruel pirate are reacting in this terrifying drama. (*She holds the microphone out to* SPIKE) Excuse me, Sir, can you describe your feelings at this point?

SPIKE: Well –

REG: Come on, come on, that's enough o' that! Get on and zap 'em, Doris, like I said!

PROFESSOR: – and I don't care *what* you say, there is no hidden treasure, and that big lever over there has nothing to do with where it isn't hidden, has it, Astra? (*Winks conspiratorially at her*)

ASTRA: Oh – er – no! Just as you say, Professor! Nothing whatever to do with hidden treasure!

REG: Lever, eh? I knew you were hidin' it somewhere! If we pull that there lever we'll find the treasure, right?

PROFESSOR: ⎱
ASTRA: ⎰ No! No!

REG: A likely story! I know the kind of double-double bluff you're tryin' to pull! But Reg the Ravager's too smart for you – right, lads?

BORIS: ⎱
HORACE: ⎰ Aye aye, Cap'n!

DORIS (*facing audience once more with her microphone*): And so we have yet another thrilling development in this exciting –

REG: Enough o' that now Doris! Just go and pull that there lever for us instead!

DORIS: Right, Captain!

DORIS *pulls the lever.*

PROFESSOR: Astra – cover your eyes!

ASTRA *covers her eyes. The stage is bathed in a strong coloured light. All except the* PROFESSOR *and* ASTRA *fall fast asleep although they remain standing.* REG, HORACE *and* BORIS *snore loudly.*

PROFESSOR: Switch it off, Astra; that'll be enough.

ASTRA, *still shielding her eyes, pushes the lever back to its original position. Coloured light fades, normal lighting resumes.*

PROFESSOR: Excellent! Now, if you'll excuse me, I'll just escort these pirates to my transporter and beam them back to their own ship before they wake up, confound the blighters!

ASTRA: Go ahead, Professor. I'll wake up the others in the meantime.

The PROFESSOR *lines up the pirates,* REG *first,* DORIS *last, and leads them off-stage blind-man's-buff style. He encourages them with 'Off you go!' and similar polite remarks.* ASTRA *is left alone with the sleeping forms of* SPIKE, STELLA *and* CORNELIA.

ASTRA: At last! The Professor will be out of sight for a few minutes – now to contact headquarters!

She pulls out a small box with a little aerial on it and twiddles some controls before speaking into it.

ASTRA: This is Astra calling Tyrantula! Astra calling Tyrantula! Come in Tyrantula!

A female voice replies. The audience will hear it through loudspeakers while ASTRA *responds as if it comes from her little transmitter.*

VOICE (TYRANTULA's; *it resembles Mrs Thatcher's, or that of any such other well-known and forceful female personality*): This is Tyrantula to Astra!

ASTRA (*promptly dropping to her knees*): Hail, Mistress of the cosmos, Queen of the time-zones, Sovereign of the sidereal wisdom –

TYRANTULA: Oh, shut up, insect, and stop grovelling!

ASTRA (*scrambling up*): Yes, O Queen –

TYRANTULA: On second thoughts, grovelling suits you. Back on your knees, worm!

ASTRA (*dropping back down*): I obey, O Tyrantula, Supreme Time Which, Sovereign of –

TYRANTULA: That will do! Silence, maggot!

ASTRA *starts twitching violently.*

TYRANTULA: No, no! I don't mean *turn into* a maggot, you fool! (ASTRA *stops twitching*) Honestly, just because you're a Tylurian chameleon doesn't mean you have to change shape *all* the time. Anyone would think you preferred your own disgusting lizard shape to being humanoid.

ASTRA: But these humanoid shapes are so horrible, O my Queen! Couldn't I be a nice lizard like the Venusians and spy for you on Venus instead?

TYRANTULA: Complaints, ha! Enough! I thought you Tylurians were supposed to be *professional* spies, genetically conditioned to all aspects of the job!

ASTRA: We are, O my Queen! We're the best!

TYRANTULA: Well, then. Now, give me a report on your present mission. Have you captured the Earthlings and the Omegan?

ASTRA: Yes, O my Queen.

TYRANTULA: And does my stupid, goody-goody cousin the Doctor –

ASTRA: Doctor? Who's that, O my Queen?

TYRANTULA: Who? Oh, I forgot. That's the other do-gooder. I mean What.

ASTRA: What do you mean, O my Queen?

TYRANTULA: That's right.

ASTRA: What's right?

TYRANTULA (*in sudden rage*): No he's not! *I'm* right! *I* am rightful commander of the M.A.S.T.E.R. space-time craft! *I* am rightful ruler of Time! I am – oh, now you've got me going again, you stupid reptile! I am referring to my cousin and rival Time Lord, Professor What. Does he suspect you are my spy?

ASTRA: No, O my Queen. He still thinks I am the girl from the planet Alpha, the humanoid who assists him, Princess Astra.

TYRANTULA: The one I launched into space from a time-catapult? (*Laughs*) That was *fun*.

ASTRA: O my Queen! I hear the Professor approaching!

TYRANTULA: Report again soon, worm. I want those Earthlings to ruin him, just as I planned! (*Laughs maniacally*)

ASTRA: Of course, O my Queen . . . (*Switches off the transmitter*) Grumpy old ratbag! I *hate* this job! I hate spying! Still, if I don't do it, what will my Mum and Dad think? I can't let down my planet's reputation – and we Tylurians are supposed to be the best spies in the whole universe!

Enter the PROFESSOR.

PROFESSOR: Good, that's those unsavoury specimens dealt with! Haven't the others woken up yet, Astra?

ASTRA: Oh, sorry, Professor! They seem to be taking longer than usual . . . I'll just help them along.

ASTRA *presses a convenient button on the control panel and immediately the sound of tinkling bells is heard for five seconds*

or so. SPIKE, STELLA *and* CORNELIA *then awake,
blinking and yawning, from their sleep.*

SPIKE: Oh, what a lovely dream! I dreamt I was listening to
sweet cosmic music, sipping ice-cool astro-juice and
settling down to a delicious space-burger!

STELLA: Me too!

CORNELIA: And me!

SPIKE: But . . . Wait a minute . . . there was a pirate . . .

STELLA: That's right! Reg the Ridiculous – or something?

CORNELIA: No, I remember! Reg the Ravager.

SPIKE: Whoever he was, he's gone now. What happened?

PROFESSOR: Well, it's really quite simple. We just tricked
the gentleman, er, 'Reg the Ravager' (*he chuckles*) into
switching on our sleep-ray, the one we use for journeys of
several light-years. Doesn't work on me, of course, being
a Time Lord, but it put them to sleep.

SPIKE: Professor, what's all this 'Time Lord' business? I
think we're owed an explanation for –

ASTRA (*urgently*): Professor, the tele-screen! Look! A star is
approaching at warp speed – it's going to hit us!

*Pop music of a sugary kind is heard playing in the
background, and it grows louder as they speak.*

ASTRA: What shall we do, Professor? Quick!

They all 'freeze'. Lights dim and music stops. Spotlight on
SANDY.

SANDY (*to audience*): Let's see now, what do we do here!
(*Reads from the book*) It says here: 'Choose your path. Do
you:
  a) go straight ahead;
  b) turn back;
  c) switch off the telescreen and put on a video instead?
Well, I don't much fancy turning back and being chased

around the universe by some rampaging star. Hmm . . .
have we got time for a video, I wonder –

CORNELIA: Sandy!

STELLA: Make your mind up – we're getting cramp here!

SANDY: Hey, watch it you lot, or I'll close the book and
leave you there! Now, where was I? Oh, yes. I think I'll
go straight ahead. 'Choice a), turn to page fifty-six' . . .

    SANDY *goes back to the book, spotlight dims. Normal
lighting up,* CHARACTERS *'unfreeze', pop music starts
again.*

PROFESSOR: What shall we do? We'll just keep going
straight ahead, Astra.

SPIKE: No, Professor!

STELLA: He's crazy!

CORNELIA: Don't do it!

ASTRA (*woodenly*): Straight ahead it is, Professor. (*To the
others, bravely*) Trust him. He must know what he's
doing.

    *There is a blinding flash of light as the pop music gets louder,
then a series of popping noises, followed by silence.*

CORNELIA: Wow! That was close!

SPIKE: How did you know we'd be safe, Professor?

PROFESSOR: Oh, I knew it would disintegrate before we
collided. This kind of star often flares up but never lasts
long.

STELLA: What kind of stars?

PROFESSOR: Pop stars!

    Others groan.

PROFESSOR: Now, my friends, suppose you explain to
me who those unpleasant ruffians were that you were
fleeing from when we took you aboard the
M.A.S.T.E.R.?

SPIKE: Oh, the Groundlings!

PROFESSOR: Groundlings?

SPIKE: Yes. We're all trainees at the interplanetary space-school. Parents from all over the Universe send their kids there in the hope that they will qualify as starship pilots and commanders.

CORNELIA: Unfortunately we sometimes get the kids of space-pirates who slip through the net and become trainees too.

PROFESSOR: Because they want to use the starship skills for piracy?

STELLA: That's right, but they usually get found out and are grounded until they can be sent home.

CORNELIA: They nearly always fail the aptitude test, you see.

PROFESSOR: And that's why they're called 'Groundlings'?

SPIKE: Correct, Sir. Unfortunately, they get so jealous of successful trainees –

STELLA: Like us.

SPIKE: – that all they want to do is bash us up.

PROFESSOR: The blackguards!

ASTRA: Professor, they don't use words like that any more in this time-zone!

PROFESSOR: Don't they? Oh dear, it's so easy to get the time-zones muddled up!

SPIKE: Time-zones again! Professor, can you please now explain what's going on?

CORNELIA: This should be fascinating.

PROFESSOR: Yes, of course I can tell you whatever you like, pop-stars and pirates permitting! What do you want to know?

STELLA: Well, how about starting with this – whatever it is – that we're inside? First it's a rubbish skip, then it's a spaceship! What is it?

PROFESSOR: This is the M.A.S.T.E.R.

CORNELIA: ⎫
STELLA: ⎬ The Master?
SPIKE: ⎭

ASTRA: Those are its initials, it stands for –

PROFESSOR: 'Mucking About with Space, Time and Everything Relative'.

CORNELIA: It's a time-machine.

PROFESSOR: Just so.

ASTRA: And it's a spaceship.

STELLA: Cosmic!

SPIKE: So we can go any time, any place, anywhere?

ASTRA: Yes, it's the real thing.

PROFESSOR: Or at least, it should be, except that we're having a spot of minor mechanical trouble – we'd stopped to check it up when we saw you on our monitors and we just had to help.

STELLA: Well, we're glad you did! Or we'd have been history ourselves, if those Groundlings had got us. Thanks, Professor!

CORNELIA: Yes indeed.

SPIKE: Yes, thank you!

PROFESSOR: It was nothing. But I'm afraid you'll have to stay with us now, until our technical faults have all been sorted out.

STELLA: Oh no!

SPIKE: How long will that take?

PROFESSOR (*shrugging*): As long as is needed. A few thousand years, possibly.

SPIKE: ⎫
STELLA: ⎬ (*horrified*): A few thousand years!
CORNELIA: ⎭

ASTRA: But don't worry; when the M.A.S.T.E.R. is back in working order we can skip across time and space to wherever you like, so you won't have to wait long really.

PROFESSOR: And I was wondering if you might like to help us fix the problem while you're here.

CORNELIA: I'd love to try! I love computers and things like that.

STELLA: Huh, I reckon you're half-computer yourself, with all the top marks you get – brainbox!

SPIKE: Stella's right, Cornelia here *is* a bit of a whizz-kid. And we'd like to help too.

PROFESSOR: Excellent!

SPIKE: But you still haven't told us exactly who *you* are –

There is a flashing of lights and a bumping sound.

PROFESSOR: And you'll have to wait a little longer still, I'm afraid. We've landed! Everybody out! Everybody out!

Lights down.

Scene 4

A forest. BEETHOVEN *is sitting under a tree with a quill in his hand, fussing over a manuscript. He speaks with a strong German accent.*

BEETHOVEN: (*humming the first three notes of the famous Fifth Symphony and getting the fourth totally wrong. He waves his hands in despair*): Nein! Nein! I must haf der inspiration! (*Hums wrongly again*) Ach! Nein! Nein! Here I am, der greatest composer in der vorld, Ludwig van Beethoven, und onto my fifth symphony already, und mein inspiration she is kaput! (*He tries again, humming the first few bars of 'My Way' or something equally ludicrous*) Mein Gott! Zat vas der vorst yet! Der vorld und such rubbish should never acqvainted be!

Enter HANS *the butler. He looks exactly like Frankenstein's monster à la Boris Karloff, but dressed in butler's uniform.*

BEETHOVEN: Ah, Hans! Your master, der Baron von Frankenstein und old friend of mein, is to be thanked indeed for letting me stay on his estate for a bit of der peace und der qviet.

HANS: Urgh!

BEETHOVEN: Ja, ja! (*to audience*) He is not much of a talker zis von, but he is ein vonderful man-servant – und good staff are so hard to find zese days. I vonder vhere der Baron von Frankenstein dug him up . . .?

HANS (*gruffly*): You rang, master?

BEETHOVEN: Ja, Hans – ein cup of tea, please, mit lots of body in it. Maybe zat vill help mit der inspiration! Der situation she is grave at der moment!

HANS: Urgh!

Exit the lumbering HANS. BEETHOVEN *tries another unsuccessful attempt at his fifth symphony. Enter* ASTRA *followed by* SPIKE, CORNELIA *and* STELLA, *unseen by* BEETHOVEN *who has returned to his meditations.*

ASTRA: According to the M.A.S.T.E.R. we have arrived somewhere in Germany in the early nineteenth century.

CORNELIA: Fascinating!

SPIKE: Yes, this time travelling is really weird!

CORNELIA: No, I mean that man sitting under that tree.

STELLA: What about him?

CORNELIA: I can hear him humming the first few bars of Beethoven's Fifth Symphony, but he keeps getting it wrong. A pity, because Beethoven's my favourite composer.

STELLA: You always were old-fashioned! I like real music like Brett Starr and his Asteroid Rappers! (*She breaks into an impromptu rap rhythm and dances until* CORNELIA *interrupts her.*)

CORNELIA: Yes, but it just so happens that they won't be around for another few hundred years! Right now is the time that Beethoven was at his peak.

BEETHOVEN (*throwing down his manuscript in disgust*): Der inspiration, she just von't come! (*He notices the others*) Oh, hello! Und whom haf I der pleasure of meeting?

CORNELIA: Excuse me, Sir, what's that tune you're humming?

SPIKE: Excuse her, Sir, Cornelia is music-mad.

BEETHOVEN: Mad? She doesn't look mad, but her ears – zey look like der tuning-forks! Ja, zat tune she is mein own . . .

CORNELIA (*in wonderment*): Are – are you – Ludwig van Beethoven?

BEETHOVEN (*modestly*): Jawohl! I am he!

CORNELIA (*reverently*): Wow! This is a great honour, Sir!

BEETHOVEN: Pardon?

CORNELIA (*loudly*): I said this is a great honour, Sir!

BEETHOVEN: Ja, ja! I may be a little hard of der hearing but zere is no need to be shouting!

ASTRA: We're all honoured to meet you, Sir.

BEETHOVEN: Mein Ladies und Sirs, der honour she is mutual – but who are you, mein friends?

CORNELIA: We, Sir, are the people who can help you with your inspiration.

BEETHOVEN: Ah, mein inspiration she is gone for der snoozes!

CORNELIA: But I can help you with that melody, Sir, it goes:

Enter PROFESSOR WHAT, *wearing a Kaiser Wilhelm spiked helmet and uniform.*

CORNELIA (*humming first three notes of the Fifth Symphony*): Da da da –
PROFESSOR: Stop!

BEETHOVEN: Donner und Blitzen! Einen crazy person!

CORNELIA: What's the matter, Professor?

SPIKE: You look worried!

PROFESSOR: I am indeed worried! You must not reveal the rest of that tune!

SPIKE: Why not?

PROFESSOR: You will interfere with the Prime Directive!

Lights dim, characters 'freeze'. Spotlight on SANDY.

SANDY: Prime Directive? What's all this about? I wonder what would happen if Cornelia did reveal the tune? Let's see the choices:
   'a) Let Cornelia reveal the tune and interfere with the Prime Directive;
   b) Stop Cornelia revealing the tune;
   c) Teach Beethoven some Richard Clayderman tunes instead.'
Yuk! Not c), anyway! But why not try a)? Let me see, for choice a) 'turn to page thirty-two' . . .

Spotlight dims, main lights up, characters 'unfreeze'.

CORNELIA: Don't be silly, Professor, what harm could it do? Herr van Beethoven, try this: (*humming the first four notes of the Fifth Symphony*) Da da da daah!

PROFESSOR: You fool! You have interfered with the laws of time itself!

BEETHOVEN: Time? Time? You call zat keeping time? Such timing is der timing of der nincompoop! Beethoven plays only his own compositions, not zose of his jealous rivals! But vait! Vat is happening?

The PROFESSOR and the OTHERS watch anxiously as BEETHOVEN puts his hands to his head and closes his eyes in a long moment of concentration.

BEETHOVEN: Ja! I haf it! Der inspiration she is come bach! Der tune I dismissed earlier – zis is der von! (*He hums a few bars of 'My Way' or whatever*) Jawohl! Zat tune she vill kill zem! Ha!

The others put their hands to their ears in horror as BEETHOVEN *launches into a full rendering of 'My Way'.*

PROFESSOR: Aagh! The future is ruined!

Spotlight up on SANDY *as she shouts.*

SANDY (*slamming the book shut*): No! Stop!

Main lights down. CHARACTERS *'freeze'.*

SANDY: Ugh! No! I can't let that happen! (*Sighs of relief heard from the stage*) Thank goodness, it looks as if I get a second chance to choose – I'll try b) instead, 'Stop Cornelia revealing the tune'. (*She opens the book again, cautiously*) Let me see, 'turn to page seventy' . . .

Spotlight dims, main lights up, CHARACTERS *'unfreeze'.*

STELLA: Prime Directive? What's the Prime Directive, Professor?

The PROFESSOR *signals them* ALL *to one side so that* BEETHOVEN *cannot hear them.*

PROFESSOR: The Prime Directive is the first rule of time travel. It absolutely forbids interference with the past – or the future, but especially the past.

SPIKE: But why, Professor?

CORNELIA: Ah, I see, because if we change the course of history all kinds of disastrous things could happen!

STELLA: Such as?

PROFESSOR: Well, if we change the past, the future would
be different and *we* might be different – worse still, we
might not be here at all!

STELLA: This is giving me brain-ache!

BEETHOVEN (*stepping towards them*): Vat is all zis, ein
secret society? Who is der von mit der cello-spike on his
noodle? Und speak up – mein hearing she is not so good!

*There is a loud sound of gunshots and wild shouting heard off-
stage. Enter* REG THE RAVAGER *with* HORACE *and*
BORIS.

REG: Ar! Is your hearing up to hearing *that*, then? Stick 'em
up, you lubbers!

SPIKE: It's Reg the Ravager! Where did he come from?

ASTRA: I thought we'd got rid of him!

REG: Rid of us? No fear, eh, lads?

HORACE: ⎫
BORIS: ⎬ (*vigorously*): Ar, Cap'n!

BEETHOVEN: Mein Gott in Himmel! More strudels mit
der flipped noodles!

ASTRA (*to* PROFESSOR): Professor, did you switch off
their tractor-beam last time we saw them?

PROFESSOR: Tractor-beam? Oh dear, I forgot! That means
we've been towing them all through time and space!

REG: That's enough o' that whispering! Now then, where's
all the treasure? It should be mine!

BEETHOVEN: Der time? She is tvelve noon.

REG: Who's this daft old space-buzzard?

CORNELIA: How dare you call the great Beethoven a
space-buzzard?

REG: Ar! We've got a game 'un 'ere!

SPIKE: Be careful, Cornelia.

HORACE: ⎫
BORIS: ⎬ Let's zap 'em, Cap'n!

PROFESSOR (*loudly*): If he's a space-buzzard then YOU ARE ONE TOO!

ASTRA: Be careful, Professor – he's dangerous!

REG: What did you say?

PROFESSOR (*more loudly*): I said if he's a space-buzzard then YOU ARE ONE TOO!

REG: Oh no I'm not!

PROFESSOR:
ASTRA:
SPIKE: } OH YES YOU ARE ONE TOO!
STELLA:
CORNELIA:

REG (*beginning to get really angry*): Oh no I'm not!

HORACE: } (*enjoying themselves*): OH YES YOU ARE
BORIS; } ONE TOO!

REG (*furious*): Right, I've 'ad enough! Time for some zappin – and you'll get zapped and like it!

As he raises his gun, enter a small robot in the 'Star Wars' tradition with the letters 'UR12' painted boldly across it in clear view of the audience. REG pauses a moment in surprise.

UR12 (*in a metallic voice*): I am here, Master.

REG (*roaring*): We're not going to be stopped by any bucket o' bolts! Zap it, lads!

HORACE and BORIS fire their ray-guns at UR12 but the robot is quite impervious to their blasts. It zaps REG, HORACE and BORIS with its own ray and they instantly fall asleep as they stand.

BEETHOVEN: Und I vanted der peace und der qviet!

PROFESSOR indicates BEETHOVEN to UR12 who zaps him. BEETHOVEN flops down into his old sitting

position under the tree. He is of course fast asleep. Enter
DORIS, *camera at the ready.*

DORIS: Sorry I'm late, folks, I was just replacing the
batteries.

   PROFESSOR *indicates* DORIS *and* UR12 *turns the ray-
gun on her.*

DORIS (*turning to make a rapid exit*): Uh-oh!

   She is not quick enough and UR12 *fires.* DORIS *falls asleep
like the others.*

PROFESSOR: That will be all, thank you, UR12.

   Exit UR12.

STELLA: Wow. That was brilliant!
SPIKE: What was that?
PROFESSOR: Oh, that? That was my droid. I always carry
one. They're so handy to have around, you know. (*To*
ASTRA) I'll take care of these (*indicating the* PIRATES)
and transport them back.
CORNELIA: But what about Beethoven?
PROFESSOR: Oh, him? Don't worry. He won't remember
seeing any of us; UR12's sleep ray has seen to that. Let's
go, everybody, back to the M.A.S.T.E.R.

   They lead the PIRATES *and* DORIS *off-stage,* ASTRA
leads.

ASTRA (*pausing*): I'll be with you in a minute, Professor!
PROFESSOR (*turning just before his exit*): Don't be long,
Astra!

   Exit ALL *but* ASTRA *and the sleeping* BEETHOVEN.
ASTRA *takes out her small transmitter and begins to twiddle
with the dials; then she pauses, frowning, and shaking her head
stuffs it back into her pocket.*

ASTRA (*to audience*): My boss, Tyrantula, wants me to spy on the Professor so that she can steal the M.A.S.T.E.R.'s vital time programming. She's already made off with some of the vital components – one more and she'll have the complete program! Then she can rule all time by herself! But I *like* the Professor! Tyrantula hopes that those nice space cadets will cause him to interfere with the Prime Directive, because she knows he is too honourable to travel through time ever again if he does. But I like *them* too! Oh, what am I going to do? (*She starts to cry*) Oh, what am I to do?

Exit ASTRA *in tears. Enter* HANS *from the other side, lumbering in with* BEETHOVEN's *cup of tea.*

HANS (*loudly and gruffly*): Your tea, Master!
BEETHOVEN (*waking up*): Huh? Oh! (*He views the tea with delight*) Ah, good, good! (*He takes the tea and sips appreciatively*) Ah, Hans, you are mein soul und inspiration!
HANS (*in gruff modesty*): What, me? Your soul and inspiration? Ha ha ha ha–ah! (*His sonorous laughter reproduces exactly the first four notes of Beethoven's Fifth Symphony.* BEETHOVEN *raises his hands rapturously in inspired recognition, and begins to scribble happily. Lights down.*)

Scene 5

Woodland with a temple in Ancient Greece. Enter ASTRA *who is moping and sighing repeatedly; she crosses the stage and exits from the other side. Enter* PROFESSOR WHAT, SPIKE, CORNELIA *and* STELLA. *The* PROFESSOR *is dressed in modern Greek national costume.*

STELLA: Who'd have thought it would be that simple, eh?

CORNELIA: It was simply a matter of reversing the polarities of the integral diodes and then re-stabilising the circuit chips.

STELLA (*ironically*): Oh, of course. A child of three could have done it.

PROFESSOR: I'm afraid, my dear, that three-year-old children were not available to us. But fortunately that brilliant and talented young scientist Cornelia *was* – in short, the M.A.S.T.E.R. has been fixed!

CORNELIA *looks modest.*

SPIKE: ⎫
STELLA: ⎬ Hooray!

PROFESSOR: And that means we can now travel wherever and whenever we like instead of losing control like before.

STELLA: So can we go home now?

PROFESSOR: Soon, my dear.

STELLA: How soon?

SPIKE: Wait a minute, Stella – I still want to ask the Professor my very first question! Professor – just who are you?

PROFESSOR: I am a Time Lord. We are beings appointed to make sure that the Prime Directive is never interferred with so that the universe is not reduced to chaos.

SPIKE: And you use your Time Machine to check up on things?

PROFESSOR: Precisely.

SPIKE: And what are we doing *here*, exactly? Not just to keep us from those Groundlings, surely?

PROFESSOR: Ah, that was merely good luck for you. In fact, I have brought the M.A.S.T.E.R. here in hot pursuit of my cousin and rival Time Lord, the Time Which Tyrantula.

SPIKE:
STELLA: } Tyrantula?
CORNELIA:

PROFESSOR: Yes, that's what she calls herself now. She used to be ever so nice, and we used to help each other, but lately she seems to have changed completely.

CORNELIA: In what way, Professor?

PROFESSOR: Well, instead of being good she wants to rule the Universe by controlling Time itself. She's taken to talking in a funny voice and laughing like a maniac whenever Time is mentioned. Poor girl.

SPIKE: So why are you chasing after her?

PROFESSOR: I'm afraid, dear boy, that she has stolen some of the vital programming circuits from the M.A.S.T.E.R. – though of course, thanks to Cornelia here we don't need them any more!

STELLA: What does she want with them?

PROFESSOR: She wants to transform her old model time machine into one as good as the M.A.S.T.E.R. so that she can carry out her plans – and she'll do it too, if I don't stop her.

STELLA: Ooh, the rotten old ratbag!

PROFESSOR (*sadly*): I can't think why she's changed. However, her plan is to get me to break the rule of the Prime Directive by allowing myself to be influenced by the people I help – like yourselves.

SPIKE: Could it work, Professor?

PROFESSOR: It could – but only if I let it. I'm here to help you fulfil your destinies, not to change them.

CORNELIA: Professor, I can hear Astra approaching, and she's crying.

PROFESSOR: Yes, my dear girl – and I know why. Quick, hide everybody – over there, and be quiet!

They hide behind a bush or any convenient stage prop. Enter ASTRA, still moping.

ASTRA: Here's a quiet spot – I suppose I'll have to contact her again. Oh, I hate doing this! (*Takes out her transmitter*) Astra to Tyrantula – come in Tyrantula –

TYRANTULA (*heard over loudspeaker as before*): Tyrantula here. What is your report, worm?

ASTRA: Hail, O my Queen of the Time Zones, Mistress of the Cosmos, Sovereign –

TYRANTULA: Yes, yes, we know all that! Have the Earthlings made the Professor break the rule of the Prime Directive yet?

ASTRA: They nearly succeeded when they met Beethoven, your Evilness, but the Professor stopped them.

TYRANTULA: Curses! The interfering old fool – I'll have to work on him myself – if you want something done, do it yourself, that's what it all boils down to.

ASTRA: At what time will you do that, your Nastiness?

TYRANTULA: Time? Time? (*She laughs maniacally*) I shall rule Time, not that old fool! Time will be mine – mine – MINE! (*More maniacal laughter*) Oh, badness! I mustn't get excited. Keep in touch, vermin, for further details. Time Which Tyrantula out.

   ASTRA *puts away her transmitter.*

ASTRA (*sadly*): Oh, what am I to do?

   The PROFESSOR *and the* OTHERS *step out from their hiding place.*

PROFESSOR: Don't worry, my dear – we'll help you.

ASTRA: Professor! How – What –

PROFESSOR: We know all about your being a reluctant spy for Tyrantula.

CORNELIA: My Omegan ears picked up your last transmission.

STELLA: } Cornelia!
SPIKE:

CORNELIA: I thought it best to tell the Professor first. Sorry, Captain Spike.

SPIKE: That's all right. I think Space Cadet Regulations would allow that in the circumstances.

ASTRA: Oh, you must hate me for being a spy!

PROFESSOR: We know you're not a bad girl, Astra, but from now on, you're not working for Tyrantula, you're working for me. And you're not a spy, you're a private detective.

ASTRA: Do you mean it, Professor?

PROFESSOR: I do.

ASTRA: Ooh, lovely!

PROFESSOR: And first, let's rescue the *real* Astra. We've been able to monitor Tyrantula's craft since the M.A.S.T.E.R.'s been fully functional, and we are almost certain that the real Astra has been time-catapulted to this location.

STELLA: Where's that then?

CORNELIA: We're in Ancient Greece – hey, I hear voices!

PROFESSOR: Hide! Quick, Astra, back to the M.A.S.T.E.R. – you'll have to watch us from there!

Exit ASTRA. *The* OTHERS *resume their former hiding places. Enter two Greek* SOLDIERS *escorting two young Greek girl* PRISONERS. *They stop in front of the temple and leave the weary-looking prisoners there.*

SOLDIER 1: Sorry, love.

GIRL 1: S'all right.

SOLDIER 2: Yeah, sorry darlin'.

GIRL 2: Not your fault.

Pause. They all sigh.

SOLDIER 1: I dunno, it's dragon this –

SOLDIER 2: – monster that –

SOLDIER 1: – and they all want the same thing –

SOLDIER 1: ⎫
SOLDIER 2: ⎭ Village maidens!

GIRLS *look with pity at the* SOLDIERS.

GIRL 1: Poor things!

GIRL 2 (*to soldiers*): Cheer up!

SOLDIER 1: Cheer up she says! It's 'er that's gettin' sacrificed!

GIRL 1: Me too!

SOLDIER 2: Both of you –

SOLDIER 1: – and you're trying to cheer *us* up!

GIRL 1: We know it's not your fault. It's that great stupid dragon's fault!

GIRL 2: Give 'im 'is due, love. He may be a great big 'orrible smelly dragon, I grant you, but he ain't stupid.

GIRL 1: S'pose not. Greedy, then.

GIRL 2: And cruel.

GIRL 1: Yeah.

SOLDIER 1 (*sobbing loudly*): Leave it out, girls!

SOLDIER 2 (*joining in*): It's breakin' our 'earts!

Enter KING ODYSSEUS *and* QUEEN PENELOPE.
The SOLDIERS *stand to attention.*

KING: All right, lads, at ease. (*The* SOLDIERS *relax.*)
Bring in the third sacrifice.

Exit SOLDIERS.

QUEEN: Poor dears!

KING (*to girls*): Sorry, girls. You know how it is.

GIRL 1: ⎫
GIRL 2: ⎭ S'all right, your Majesty.

KING: Been studying your dictionaries, then?

GIRL 1: ⎫
GIRL 2: ⎭ Yeah.

GIRL 2: Not that that'll do much good.
KING: Don't be like that, girls!

Enter SOLDIERS with the real ASTRA – the same actress in a different costume.

SOLDIER 1 (*toneless*): Princess Astra for sacrifice –

PROFESSOR and the OTHERS emerge from their hiding place and step forward. The GREEKS stare and the SOLDIERS draw their swords.

ASTRA: Professor What!
KING: Who are you? Do you know this girl? (*indicating* ASTRA)
PROFESSOR: Indeed we do! She is the lost Princess Astra, and we have been searching far and wide for her! But don't be alarmed – allow us to introduce ourselves. I am the Professor, and these are my companions Stella, Spike and Cornelia.
KING (*to SOLDIERS*): Okay, lads, they don't seem dangerous.

SOLDIERS put away their weapons.

KING (*to PROFESSOR*): I am Odysseus, King of this Greek island, and this is my Queen, Penelope.
QUEEN: How do?

The PROFESSOR, SPIKE, STELLA and CORNELIA bow politely. The KING looks very hard at CORNELIA.

KING: This one has ears like Pan!
CORNELIA: They're quite common where I come from.
PROFESSOR: Your Majesty, what do you intend to do with these girls?
KING: I'm afraid they have to be sacrificed.

SPIKE:
STELLA: } Sacrificed?
CORNELIA:

QUEEN: You men are all the same! Why must it always be the girls that are sacrificed?

STELLA: Yeah!

KING (*looking pained*): But that's the way it's always been. It's *tradition*!

QUEEN: Tradition – huh! (*snapping her fingers*) That for tradition!

KING: Penny, darling . . .!

QUEEN: Shove off, Odie!

PROFESSOR: Your Majesty – why are they being sacrificed?

KING: They must be sacrificed to the dreadful monster Thesaurus, the Pun-Dragon!

CORNELIA (*to* PROFESSOR): Pun-dragons? I've heard of them!

PROFESSOR (*to* CORNELIA): In a minute, my girl. (*To the* KING) Tell us more, your Majesty.

KING: It's an occupational hazard in Greece, I'm afraid, dragons or monsters of one sort or another. A few years ago it was young Perseus who rescued Andromeda from a dragon; then there was Oedipus who got rid of the Sphinx . . . nasty creature that – half-lion, half-human and killed you if you couldn't answer its riddles.

SOLDIER 1: Sounds like my drill-sergeant.

KING: Then this thing comes along. It challenges us to defeat it in competitions, punning on words, and if you lose it drains your brain and leaves you like a zombie.

GIRL 1: I had a teacher like that.

KING: I thought I was good at words, but this Thesaurus takes the cake –

QUEEN: – *and* the village maidens! I've got a whole palace full of female zombies now!

GIRL 2: Sounds like my old school.

CORNELIA (*to* PROFESSOR, SPIKE *and* STELLA): I recognise this creature! It's a pun-dragon from Betelgeuse Six! They love feeding on brainwaves and they *adore* showing off! They are ancient creatures, infamous in Omegan folklore.

STELLA: Cornelia, you may be the brainbox, but I'm the one who's good at puns.

SPIKE: There'll be no heroics from you, Stella – and that's an order!

PROFESSOR: Don't argue now. The King's about to speak.

KING: Right, everybody, the invocation (*nodding at the* QUEEN): repeat after us, if you please.

All the GREEKS *apart from the* KING *and* QUEEN *kneel.*

KING:
QUEEN: } 'We summon you O dragon scary . . .'

GREEKS repeat.

KING:
QUEEN: } 'To challenge our vocabulary . . .'

GREEKS repeat.

KING;
QUEEN: } 'If you win, our minds you scoff . . .'

GREEKS repeat.

KING:
QUEEN: } 'If you lose then just clear off!'

GREEKS repeat, with utmost solemnity. A sound as of huge beating wings is heard. Enter THESAURUS THE PUN-

DRAGON, *who is like a large crocodile (preferably winged)*
wearing a smoking-jacket and smoking a cigarette in a long holder.

THESAURUS: Ooh, I thought you'd never ask! What've
we got here, then? Three of the best? Who's first?

KING: Can't you let us off this year?

THESAURUS: Ooh, I couldn't! More than my job's
worth.

QUEEN: You beast!

THESAURUS: Are you starting, then?

KING: No, she's not! There are the poor victims!

THESAURUS: Don't be like that! Relax, enjoy yourselves!

KING: But you always win!

THESAURUS (*studying his claws and polishing them*): Yes, I
do, don't I? Well, talent will out, as they say . . .

GIRL 1: Bighead!

GIRL 2: Yeah!

THESAURUS: All right, punsters – who's going to start?

GIRL 2: Oh, go on, I will.

THESAURUS: Ooh, goody! Right then, the usual rules.
We take turns to choose a subject for the other to pun on,
and the first one who can't think of an answer loses! Now
then, what pun can you make of the City of Athens?

GIRL 2: I dunno, it's all Greek to me!

THESAURUS: I like it! Your turn to choose a subject!

KING (*aside to the* PROFESSOR): That was a lucky answer!
I know that girl – she's as thick as a temple pillar!

THESAURUS: Come along, hurry up!

GIRL 2: Er – (*looks desperately around her*) er – how about
rocks? Yeah, give me a pun on rocks.

THESAURUS: Ooh. I see you're getting 'boulder' by the
minute! Get it – rocks, boulder – ooh, I amaze myself
sometimes! Now then, my turn again! Give me a pun on
– now let me see – crocodiles!

GIRL 2 (*scratching her head*): Can't think of anything – er –

THESAURUS: Right! Time's up! Time for a quick snack.

He points his cigarette-holder at the GIRL *who suddenly goes rigid with a vacant expression on her face.*

THESAURUS (*looking dissatisfied*): Hmm, not much flavour in that! Next!

GIRL 1: Who? Me?

THESAURUS: Of course you! Now then, *you* give me a pun on crocodiles!

GIRL 1 (*after a short pause*): Er – sorry – I dunno any.

THESAURUS (*not impressed*): Then I don't suppose you'll taste much better, but I can hope.

He points his cigarette-holder at her, and she goes rigid like her companion.

THESAURUS (*in disgust*): No, she tasted worse! Really, these brains must be the dregs. If I'd been asked that pun –

PROFESSOR: You'd have given a 'snappy' answer!

THESAURUS: Very good! Who said that?

PROFESSOR: I did. I challenge you.

SPIKE:
STELLA:
CORNELIA: } (*horrified*): No, Professor!
ASTRA:

PROFESSOR (*raising his voice, undeterred*): I challenge you, Thesaurus, and if I defeat you you must release all your victims and never return again!

ASTRA: No, Professor! No! We can't afford to lose one of our Time Lords!

THESAURUS (*licking his lips*): A Time Lord, eh? Now, all those brainwaves should be tasty indeed!

STELLA: No – try me instead!

THESAURUS (*kindly*) Maybe later, dear. (*To the* PROFESSOR) I accept! Let's start then – first one to fail to answer loses – two goes each. If I answer both with a pun I win anyway.

KING: Hey, that's not fair!

THESAURUS: Ah, but he's no ordinary punster, he's special, he's a Time Lord. Time – give me your first pun on Time!

PROFESSOR: Do I get any 'second' chances?

THESAURUS: Ooh, sneaky! Give me a subject, then.

PROFESSOR: Atomic energy.

THESAURUS: Oh, that's easy – and I'm not just 'fission' for compliments! Get it – fishing, fission – oh, please yourselves. My turn – and I'm sure *you*'ll have no difficulty tackling the subject of amoebas.

PROFESSOR: Don't try the 'soft-cell' approach with me! Get it – cell with a 'c'?

THESAURUS: Ugh, that's awful!

PROFESSOR: Thank you. My turn. But what shall I choose? I'll give you a choice, Thesaurus. You can have as a subject either: a) terminal skin disease in fish; or b) Scandinavia. What's it to be?

Lights dim, all 'freeze', spotlight on SANDY.

SANDY: Oh goodness! If Thesaurus makes a pun out of this he'll get to drain the Professor's brainwaves! I'll have to make sure I choose the more difficult subject . . . surely choice a) would be best? Nobody could make a pun on 'Terminal skin-disease in fish'! Right, 'turn to page eighty-four' . . .

Spotlight down, main lights up, CHARACTERS *'unfreeze'.*

PROFESSOR: Well, what's it to be?

THESAURUS (*drawling*): Terminal skin disease in fish, old boy? Now that's what I call a 'full-scale' disaster – for the fish! (*reverting rapidly to his old voice as others groan*) I win! I win! Ooh, I'm going to have *such* a feast here! (*He waves his cigarette-holder over all the company, who one by one go rigid and blank, and lastly over the* PROFESSOR) Ah! (*He gives a loud belch*) Exquisite!

He exits laughing loudly; lights dim, spotlight on SANDY.

SANDY (*staring down at the page*): 'The End.' 'The End'? The book can't finish like that! What about Tyrantula? What about the Groundlings? Whoops, I think I made the wrong choice.

STELLA (*her voice coming from the darkness on stage*): Yeah, 'whoops'! Thanks, Sandy – you've landed us all in Zombie-city.

SANDY (*frantically turning pages*): All right! All right! I'm going as fast as I can to choice b)! Page eighty-five – ah, found it!

Spotlight dims, main lights up, CHARACTERS *'unfreeze'.*

PROFESSOR: Well, Thesaurus, which subject will you take?

THESAURUS (*sulkily*): I don't like either of them. Oh, all, right. Give me choice b).

PROFESSOR: Choice b) – a pun on Scandinavia.

THESAURUS: And if I can't think of one, you have to, or I still win!

PROFESSOR: You didn't say that at the beginning of the game!

THESAURUS (*icily*): That was *then*. This is *now*.

PROFESSOR: Well, it's still you to start. Go on!

THESAURUS (*after a pause*): It's impossible. Nobody can think of a pun on Scandinavia, not even me! You thought up the subject – *you* give me one, or I'll scoff the lot of you!

ASTRA: Oh, no!

STELLA: He'll never do it!

PROFESSOR: What, me? Give you a pun on Scandinavia?

THESAURUS: Yes, Mr Super-clever Time Lord! You give me a pun on Scandinavia – go on!

PROFESSOR: Nor-way! Get it? No way, Norway?

Loud cheers from the GREEKS *and the* CADETS.

THESAURUS (*who has closed his eyes*): Aagh! It's awful! It's excruciating! Exquisite torture! What a truly appalling pun!

PROFESSOR: Now keep your word. Release all your victims.

THESAURUS: Right. Right! After all, what's losing a few inferior brainwaves in return for a pun like that? Just wait 'till I tell them on Betelgeuse Six!

Exit THESAURUS, *still laughing and repeating 'Norway'. The 'ZOMBIES' wake up.*

ALL: Hooray! Three cheers for the Professor!

KING: How can I reward you, Professor?

PROFESSOR: Oh, just let us take Princess Astra back. That's reward enough.

ASTRA: But Professor, I think you should know that the pun-dragon was summoned here in the first place by Tyrantula.

QUEEN: Tyrantula? Haven't we heard that name before?

KING: Yes, she's the one who told our High Priestess, Circe, that her magic was mere superstition. She called herself Miss Which then.

PROFESSOR: Tell us more!

KING: Yes, she was perfectly pleasant at first – but although she didn't mean any harm, Circe cast a spell on her for doubting her magic. She's a crusty old soul, Circe, though she means well. Anyway, the spell made Miss

Which turn into the opposite kind of person to her normal
self.

CORNELIA: Like Dr Jekyll and Mr Hyde!

PROFESSOR: Yes, a complete personality change – so
that's when the rot started! Tell me, can we get a cure for
this spell?

KING: Oh yes! Circe never meant it to be permanent, just
to prove to Miss Which that her magic was real. She was
ever so sorry afterwards that she'd lost her temper,
because although she prepared the cure – a magic powder
– it was too late: Tyrantula had already gone.

PROFESSOR: Yes, to start a whole lot of trouble! Can we
get this powder now?

KING: Of course. Follow me. You lot (*indicating*
SOLDIERS) take these village maidens home.

Exit KING, QUEEN, PROFESSOR, ASTRA, SPIKE,
STELLA *and* CORNELIA.

SOLDIER 1: Come along then, girls!

SOLDIER 2: I dunno . . . Maidens, zombies . . . can't see
much difference myself!

GIRL 1: ⎫
GIRL 2: ⎭ Cheek!

Exit laughing.

Scene 6

*The same lonely street as Scene Two. The M.A.S.T.E.R.
appears once again as a rubbish skip. Enter* ASTRA – *the real one
– and the* PROFESSOR, *now back in his smoking-jacket.*

PROFESSOR: Now keep calm, my dear, and follow the
plan. Those Groundlings we told you about will be here
any minute, and they'll distract Tyrantula – and then we
put Circe's powder on her.

ASTRA: Right, Professor.

PROFESSOR: See you shortly, then. (*He retires into the M.A.S.T.E.R.*)

ASTRA (*nervously*): See you . . .

> *Enter* TYRANTULA, *who wears a business suit and looks stern. She carries a ray-gun.*

TYRANTULA: Well, worm? You called me and now I'm here. I hope you've got something for me!

ASTRA: Oh, yes, Miss.

TYRANTULA: Miss? What's this 'Miss'? You usually call me 'Your Evilness' at least.

ASTRA: Sorry, your Evilness.

TYRANTULA: All right, then, insect; are the Earthlings and the Omegan still with you?

> *Enter* CORNELIA, SPIKE *and* STELLA *from the M.A.S.T.E.R.*

SPIKE: We're here, Tyrantula!

TYRANTULA: Well, at least you got that bit right, reptile, if nothing else –

> *Enter* PROFESSOR WHAT.

PROFESSOR: And here am I, my dear cousin, my dear Miss Which.

TYRANTULA: So we meet at last, Mr Do–Gooder! (*Points her ray-gun at him*) Well, I haven't made you break the Prime Directive yet, so I'm just going to leave you here and take the M.A.S.T.E.R. instead.

PROFESSOR: You're going to steal it?

TYRANTULA: Yes! Then I shall rule all Time . . . TIME! (*maniacal laughter*) And you will all be stranded here! But first a new improved sleep–ray that'll keep even *you* quiet.

> *Before she can fire, enter the* GROUNDLINGS *still chanting 'Smash 'em, bash 'em' etc.*

GROUNDLING 7: There they are!

GROUNDLING 5: Get 'em!

GROUNDLING 1: Wait! Who are those others? And watch it – that one's got a ray-gun!

TYRANTULA *is aiming her gun at the* GROUNDLINGS.

GROUNDLING 1: Duck!

All the GROUNDLINGS *promptly drop to the floor. Enter* REG THE RAVAGER *with* BORIS, HORACE *and* DORIS.

REG: Avast you lubbers!

TYRANTULA *is aiming her gun at* REG *now, but before she can fire it,* HORACE *creeps behind her and disarms her.*

REG: I don't know who you are lady, but I've seen these others before. They're always gettin' in me way! Right now I'm only interested in finding one person, and that's my boy!

PROFESSOR: Your boy?

REG: Ar! My son, Cyril.

STELLA: *Cyril* the Ravager?

SPIKE: Doesn't have quite the same ring to it, does it?

REG: Ar, 'e be a space cadet now!

TYRANTULA: Take your grubby offspring and go!

REG: Cyril!

GROUNDLING 10 *stands up.*

CYRIL (*still lisping*): I'm here, Pater!

REG: Ar! (*Gives* CYRIL *a hug*) Me old space-dog!

CYRIL: Thuper to thee you too, Thir!

STELLA: Ah!

TYRANTULA *is watching all this with tapping foot.*
ASTRA *tries to take advantage of her inattention and throw the*
powder over her, but DORIS *flashes her camera in* ASTRA's
face. ASTRA *staggers –* DORIS *catches hold of her wrist and*
takes the powder from her.

REG: Ar, Doris, you weren't late this time – and what a
　　scoop ah?

DORIS: You bet! (*She hands to* REG *the box of powder*)

REG: What's this 'ere stuff?

TYRANTULA (*still tapping her foot*): Why don't you clear
　　off, you smelly, verminous little man?

REG: Oi! Reg don't have to take that from nobody! (*He*
　　throws the powder – a glittery substance – over
　　TYRANTULA. *She blinks and stares around her. She has*
　　become Miss Which again and her voice returns to its proper
　　kindly tones.)

TYRANTULA: Professor! How nice to see you, cousin!

SPIKE: Well I never!

CORNELIA: What a change!

PROFESSOR: Welcome back, my dear!

REG (*scratching his head*): I don't know what's goin' on 'ere
　　but I don't want anything more to do with you and your
　　treasure. I've got meself a job now.

PROFESSOR: A job?

REG: Ar, that's right! I'm special adviser to the Space
　　Institution now. I advise them how to prevent piracy in
　　space!

STELLA: Good old Reg!

PROFESSOR: Well done, Mr Ravager.

REG: Not Ravager – not no more I'm not. And Boris and
　　Horace are my assistants.

HORACE: ⎱
　　　　　⎰ Ar!
BORIS: ⎰

STELLA: What about Doris?

REG: Ar, well, I got to realise what a fine space missus
   she'd make – she's a real game 'un!

STELLA: You don't say!

REG: Ar! She's my missis now – little Cyril 'ere needs a
   mum, since his real mum was lost wrestling Gamma-
   gators on Alpha Twelve. An' she's lovely too.

DORIS: That makes two of us then!

TYRANTULA: I'm so pleased for you both!

STELLA: But won't you miss being a pirate, Reg?

REG: Ar . . . well . . .

DORIS (*aside to* STELLA): Reg never actually managed to
   rob anybody! He's better off as he is!

REG: . . . I needed a change – I'm much better at doing this
   new job!

HORACE: Oh yeah? Wot about this grovellin' lot? (*indicates
   the* GROUNDLINGS)

REG: Avast you scurvy lubbers! (REG, BORIS *and*
   HORACE *start kicking the* GROUNDLINGS *and roaring
   at them.* GROUNDLINGS *take to their heels and exit
   screaming* 'They're madmen!' 'Criminals!' 'I'll tell me
   mum!' *and other such.* CYRIL *is left with his father.*)

REG: Well, I've no more business 'ere – 'bye, and no 'ard
   feelings!

PROFESSOR: No hard feelings, Reg – and I'm sure Cyril
   will make a fine space cadet!

SPIKE: We'll see to that, next term!

   Exit REG, DORIS, CYRIL, HORACE *and* BORIS.

PROFESSOR: Well, Miss Which, it's nice to have you back.

TYRANTULA: I'm so glad to be rid of that awful
   Tyrantula!

PROFESSOR: Tyrantula's spy – who I thought was Astra –
   is waiting for you in the M.A.S.T.E.R. She's an awfully
   nice Tylurian chameleon called Amanda really. She'd
   make you a wonderful assistant. (*Turns to the others*)

Thanks for you help, Captain Spike, Stella, Cornelia – you needn't be afraid of the Groundlings any more – Reg will have it all in hand! Goodbye! Come along, cousin, come, Astra.

ASTRA: Goodbye!

Exit MISS WHICH, ASTRA *and the* PROFESSOR.

CORNELIA:
STELLA: } Goodbye!
SPIKE:

SPIKE: And goodbye Sandy! Keep on reading those books!

ALL: Goodbye!

Lights dim. Spotlight on SANDY.

SANDY (*putting down the book*): Well! 'Playing for Time' – I enjoyed that! (*To audience*) I guess that makes me a reader of books now. And you all read the story with me, so if I'm a reader then You Are One Too! 'Bye!

Exit SANDY; *but before the lights have gone completely, enter the droid* UR12.

UR12: You called, Master?

[*Curtain*]